THE SONGS OF
JOHN DRYDEN

LONDON : HUMPHREY MILFORD

OXFORD UNIVERSITY PRESS

THE
SONGS OF
JOHN DRYDEN

EDITED BY

CYRUS LAWRENCE DAY

HARVARD UNIVERSITY PRESS
CAMBRIDGE, MASSACHUSETTS
MDCCCCXXXII

PRINTED AT THE HARVARD UNIVERSITY PRESS

CAMBRIDGE, MASS., U.S.A.

To

HYDER EDWARD ROLLINS

CONTENTS

INTRODUCTION vii

THE SONGS I

NOTES

    TEXTUAL 137

    GENERAL 141

INDEXES

    FIRST LINES 191

    NAMES AND TITLES 193

LIST OF FACSIMILES

V   Ah fading joy how quickly art thou past .   7
      [*Choice Ayres, Songs, & Dialogues*, 1675, I, 70–71]

VII   Make ready fair lady to-night 8
      [*The Village Opera*, 1729, Air XLV]

XI   Dry those eyes which are o'erflowing . . 14
      [*The Ariel's Songs in the Play Call'd the Tempest*,
        ca. 1675, No. 2]

XII   Go thy way 15
      [*The Ariel's Songs in the Play Call'd the Tempest*,
        ca. 1675, No. 3]

XIV   Hark my Damilcar we are called below . . 19
      [British Museum: Addit. MS. 19759, ff. 29^v–30]

XVIII   After the pangs of a desperate lover . . 25
      [*Choice Songs and Ayres*, 1673, p. 8]

XIX   Calm was the even and clear was the sky   27
      [*Choice Songs and Ayres*, 1673, p. 9]

XXI   Beneath a myrtle shade 31
      [*Choice Songs and Ayres*, 1673, p. 45]

XXII   Wherever I am and whatever I do 33
      [*Choice Songs and Ayres*, 1673, p. 37]

XXIII   How unhappy a lover am I 37
      [*Choice Songs and Ayres*, 1673, p. 38]

XXIV   Farewell fair Armeda my joy and my grief   39
      [*Choice Songs and Ayres*, 1673, p. 10]

XXV   Why should a foolish marriage vow 41
      [*Choice Songs and Ayres*, 1673, p. 39]

XXVI   Whilst Alexis lay pressed 43
      [*Choice Songs and Ayres*, 1673, p. 27]

XXVIII   LONG BETWIXT LOVE AND FEAR PHILLIS TORMENTED   45
[*Choice Songs and Ayres*, 1673, p. 59]

XXIX   THE DAY IS COME I SEE IT RISE   47
[*Choice Songs and Ayres*, 1673, p. 60]

XXXV   CAN LIFE BE A BLESSING.   55
[*Choice Ayres and Songs*, 1681, III, 3]

XL   FAREWELL UNGRATEFUL TRAITOR   59
[British Museum: Addit. MS. 19759, f. 20ᵛ]

XLII   TELL ME THIRSIS TELL YOUR ANGUISH   62
[*Choice Ayres and Songs*, 1683, IV, 80–81]

LIII   GO TELL AMYNTA GENTLE SWAIN   74
[*The Theater of Music*, 1685, I, 30]

LXXX   ASK NOT THE CAUSE WHY SULLEN SPRING . . .   103
[*Mercurius Musicus*, March, 1699, pp. 45–47]

LXXXII   CHLOE FOUND AMYNTAS LYING   106
[*Deliciae Musicae*, 1695, II, 2]

LXXXIII   WHAT STATE OF LIFE CAN BE SO BLEST   109
[*Thesaurus Musicus*, 1694, II, 31]

LXXXIV   YOUNG I AM AND YET UNSKILLED   111
[*The Gentleman's Journal*, January and February,
1694, p. 35]

LXXXIX   HAPPY AND FREE SECURELY BLEST   129
[British Museum: Harl. MS. 1264, ff. 78ᵛ–80[

XCII   HIGH STATE AND HONORS TO OTHERS IMPART . .   134
[*Choice Ayres and Songs*, 1683, IV, 21]

INTRODUCTION

IT IS something of a paradox that John Dryden, the greatest of English neo-classical poets, should have achieved his most enduring triumph in the field of lyrical poetry. Yet *Alexander's Feast* and the almost equally glorious *Song for St. Cecilia's Day* have been more universally applauded and are to-day more widely known than any of his other poems. We of this generation have become so thoroughly imbued with the notions of a century and more of practising Romanticists, who for our delectation have poured forth in song their variegated personalities and souls, that the possibility of objective lyrical poetry seldom occurs to us. To Dryden there was no paradox in the fact that *Alexander's Feast*, as impersonal a production as any of his satires, was esteemed by his contemporaries the best of all his poetry. "I thought so myself when I writ it," he confessed in 1697, shortly after the ode was published, "but being old, I mistrusted my own Judgment." Here too is a fact worth pondering. Dryden was sixty-six when he composed what has more than once been denominated the noblest lyric in the English language. At an age when the fire of many a more sensitive, more introspective, talent has long since burned itself to ashes, Dryden's robust neo-classical genius flared higher than ever.

Dryden's lyrical gift was his constant possession during the whole of his literary career. "Ah fading joy," which he wrote for *The Indian Emperour* in 1665, has a haunting, almost overpowering, beauty that he never in his shorter songs was able to surpass. *The Secular Masque*, possibly his last composition before his death in 1700, shows literally no decay in his peculiar powers. Nearly all of his shorter lyrics are to be found in his plays, but a few were published in successive volumes of the *Miscellany Poems*. Their variety is extraordinary, their general level of attainment astonishingly high. Again and again we come upon the most mellifluous harmonies, the loveliest felicities of phrase, — whole poems, indeed, that are almost perfect in form and expression. It was seldom that he fell below the high standard that he set for himself. But at the same time he never managed to achieve anything quite so graceful as Sedley's *Knotting Song*, so gay as Dorset's *Lines Written at Sea*, or so moving as three or four songs of Rochester's. There is a definite analogy here with his accomplishment as a dramatist. His plays represent by all odds the most characteristic and distinguished contribution to the English drama made by any one Restoration playwright; but it was reserved for Wycherley to write *The Plain Dealer*, and for Otway to write *Venice Preserved*. Just so Dryden habitually winged his lyrical flight at a level higher than his fellows were able except occasionally to attain, but momentary bursts of inspiration carried some of them at times above him.

I do not mean to imply that Dryden's songs are faultless. Too many of them, especially his most characteristic love-songs, are marred by a recurrent note of cynicism and sensuality, by an unpleasant insistence upon the physical aspects of love amounting almost to morbidity (so it seems to me), and only imperfectly concealed by the conventional euphemistic disguise in which his immodest conceptions are garbed. Dryden's use of *double entendre* is in accord with the practise of his contemporaries, but it is in bad taste for all that, and the more so because he borrows for the purpose the language of religious inspiration. So subtle are a handful of his songs that a reader uninitiated in the code of the seventeenth-century *cours d'Amour* is not at all unlikely to miss the point of some of his insinuations. I have myself at a revival of *Marriage A-la-Mode* heard one of his most indecent lyrics sung with perfect propriety because the audience, when they comprehended the indistinctly enunciated phrases at all, accepted them literally and failed to grasp their real signification. But all of Dryden's songs are not love-songs, and not all of his love-songs are, from the point of view of frankness, in such doubtful taste.

Songs are but dead, remarks "honest" John Playford in the

preface to his collection of *Choice Ayres*, 1676, unless they have
"*Airy Tunes* to quicken them." And it should be borne constantly in mind that practically all of Dryden's songs were set
to music and sung in plays or at concerts before they were
printed and offered to the reading public. Unfortunately
Dryden's career as a dramatist was nearly over before the
flowering of Henry Purcell's genius, and the older men with
whom he collaborated were all possessed, in comparison with
Purcell, of very moderate abilities. The most gifted of the numerous English composers writing for the stage during the early
years of the Restoration was probably Pelham Humphrey; but
Dryden employed him, so far as I have been able to discover,
to write the music for only two songs, "Ah fading joy" and
"Wherever I am," and he died prematurely in 1674. Robert
Smith, Alphonso Marsh, Nicholas Staggins, and other musicians
of the second and third rank, set the bulk of his theater-songs
during these years, and their compositions, while interesting
enough as guides to the musical taste of the Restoration public,
are uninspired and extremely conventional in both motif and
melodic design.

In 1685 Dryden made the mistake of inviting Louis Grabu
to compose the music for his first opera, *Albion and Albanius*.
Pelham Humphrey is said to have asserted of Grabu that "he
understands nothing, nor can play on any instrument, and so
cannot compose." And yet Charles II, whose fondness for
things French was exceeded only by his lack of musical taste,
made him Master of the Royal Music over the head of the able
native composer and violinist, John Banister. *Albion and Albanius*, at any rate, was a fiasco — in part, no doubt, because
of the death of Charles II, but chiefly because of the quality of
Grabu's music.

It was not until 1690, following the production of Betterton's
operatic version of *The Prophetess*, that Dryden learned to appreciate the merit of Henry Purcell, and invited him to write
the music for *Amphitryon*. "What has been wanting on my
Part," he says in the preface to that play, "has been abundantly
supplyed by the Excellent Composition of Mr. *Purcell*; in whose

Person we have at length found an *English-man*, equal with the best abroad. At least my Opinion of him has been such, since his happy and judicious Performance in the Late *Opera*; and the Experience I have had of him, in the setting my Three Songs for this *Amphitryon*: To all which, and particularly to the Composition of the *Pastoral Dialogue*, the numerous Quire of Fair Ladies gave so just Applause on the Third Day."

But Dryden wrote only three more dramatic pieces after *Amphitryon*, and though well seconded by Purcell in *King Arthur* and *Cleomenes*, he turned to John Eccles for the music in *Love Triumphant*. It is difficult to imagine why he broke with Purcell, for in the preface to *King Arthur* he remarks that music has been brought to a greater perfection in England than ever before, "especially passing through the Artful Hands of Mr. *Purcel*, who has Compos'd it with so great a Genius, that he has nothing to fear but by an ignorant, ill-judging Audience." Operatic versions and revivals of some of Dryden's earlier plays — *The Indian-Queen, The Indian Emperour, The Tempest, Tyrannick Love* — were produced between 1690 and 1695, and for these Purcell supplied some of his best and most typical dramatic music. But he probably worked in these instances at the request of the managers rather than of Dryden himself.

The canon of Dryden's songs is rather more definite than the ephemeral nature of such compositions would lead one to expect. To be sure, his part in the lyrical portions of the plays which he wrote in collaboration with other dramatists will probably never be exactly determined. And Professor Saintsbury has raised the question whether he did not have a hand in one or more of the songs inserted in Betterton's *Prophetess*, an adaptation from Fletcher and Massinger erroneously ascribed to Dryden by Langbaine. He certainly contributed a prologue to this opera, and the best song in it, "What shall I do to show how much I love her," seems much above the literary powers elsewhere exhibited by Betterton. Another song, "Farewell, fair Armeda, my joy and my grief," is almost as dubious, for here the internal evidence is at variance with a contemporary attribution in *The Rehearsal*. These two are the only anonymous or doubtful songs that have been ascribed to Dryden with any show of probability, and I have included them for the sake of completeness in the present edition. As for the English hymns, first printed in 1706 and assigned to Dryden on purely conjectural grounds, no evidence of a tangible nature has as yet been adduced. I have, of course, printed his translation of *Veni Creator Spiritus*, which was published under his name during his lifetime.

It has been my aim in preparing this edition to bring together within a single volume all of Dryden's songs — all of his lyrical compositions, that is to say, which he intended should be sung to the accompaniment of music. I have adopted a chronological arrangement, based upon the dates of the works (usually first editions of plays or miscellanies) from which I have derived the texts of the songs; and in the Notes at the end of the book I have presented a certain amount of previously inaccessible information concerning the earliest musical settings. I have also included facsimile reproductions, showing the contemporary musical notation, of as many of the original airs as I have been able to recover, with the following exceptions:

(1) Purcell's music for *Amphitryon*, *King Arthur*, *Cleomenes*, and other plays.

(2) Grabu's music for *Albion and Albanius*.

(3) The music by Daniel Purcell and Finger for *The Secular Masque*.

(4) Draghi's music for the 1687 ode on St. Cecilia's Day.

(5) Blow's music for the ode on the death of Henry Purcell.

Of the music in the foregoing list, that by Henry Purcell is, of course, available in *The Works of Henry Purcell*, admirably edited for the Purcell Society. The work of the remaining composers is both long and relatively tedious, and it has, for reasons of economy, seemed inexpedient to reproduce it.

The material for this edition was largely assembled while I was in England in 1930–1931 as holder of a Frederick Sheldon Fellowship in English from Harvard University. Most of the song-books, miscellanies, and single songs (or songs printed on single sheets from engraved copper plates) which I have consulted in the preparation of the volume are preserved in the British Museum, and I wish to express my gratitude for the many courtesies extended to me there, as well as at the other libraries, in particular the Bodleian Library and the Harvard College Library, where I have been privileged to pursue my studies. I wish also to acknowledge my indebtedness to Professors George Lyman Kittredge and Hyder Edward Rollins, who read the work in manuscript and generously offered many detailed and valuable suggestions for its improvement.

C. L. D.

THE SONGS OF
JOHN DRYDEN

I

You twice Ten Hundred Deities,
To whom we daily Sacrifice;
You Powers that dwell with Fate below,
And see what men are doom'd to do;
Where Elements in discord dwell;
Thou God of Sleep arise and tell
Great *Zempoalla* what strange Fate
Must on her dismal Vision wait.
By the croaking of the Toad,
In their Caves that make aboad,
Earthy *Dun* that pants for breath,
With her swell'd sides full of death;
By the Crested Adders Pride
That along the Clifts do glide;
By thy visage fierce and black;
By the Deaths-head on thy back;
By the twisted Serpents plac'd
For a Girdle round thy Waste.
By the Hearts of Gold that deck
Thy Brest, thy Shoulders, and thy Neck:
From thy sleepy Mansion rise,
And open thy unwilling Eyes,
While bubling Springs their Musick keep,
That use to lull thee in thy sleep.

[*The Indian-Queen*, 1665, ACT III]

II

Poor Mortals that are clog'd with Earth below
    Sink under Love and Care,
    While we that dwell in Air
Such heavy Passions never know.
    Why then shou'd Mortals be
    Unwilling to be free
    From Blood, that sullen Cloud,
    Which shining Souls does shroud?
        Then they'l shew bright,
        And like us light,
When leaving Bodies with their Care,
    They slide to us and Air.

[*The Indian-Queen*, 1665, ACT III]

III

SONG.

You to whom Victory we owe,
    Whose glories rise
    By sacrifice,
    And from our fates below;
Never did yet your Altars shine
Feasted with Blood so nere divine;
    Princes to whom we bow,
    As they to you,
These you can ravish from a throne,
And by their loss of power declare your own.

[*The Indian-Queen*, 1665, ACT V]

IV

I look'd and saw within the Book of Fate,
   Where many days did lower,
   When lo one happy hour
Leapt up, and smil'd to save thy sinking State:
   A day shall come when in thy power
   Thy cruel Foes shall be;
   Then shall thy Land be free,
   And thou in Peace shall Raign:
But take, O take that opportunity,
Which once refus'd will never come again.

               [*The Indian Emperour*, 1667, ACT II]

V

SONG.

1

Ah fading joy, how quickly art thou past?
   Yet we thy ruine haste:
As if the cares of Humane Life were few
   We seek out new:
And follow Fate that does too fast pursue.

2

See how on every bough the Birds express
   In their sweet notes their happiness.
   They all enjoy, and nothing spare;

But on their Mother Nature lay their care:
Why then should Man, the Lord of all below
　　Such troubles chuse to know
As none of all his Subjects undergo?

3

Hark, hark, the Waters fall, fall, fall;
And with a Murmuring sound
Dash, dash, upon the ground,
　　To gentle slumbers call.

　　　　　[*The Indian Emperour*, 1667, ACT IV]

VI

Song.

I

I feed a flame within which so torments me
That it both pains my heart, and yet contents me:
'Tis such a pleasing smart, and I so love it,
That I had rather die, than once remove it.

2

Yet he for whom I grieve shall never know it,
My tongue does not betray, nor my eyes show it:
Not a sigh nor a tear my pain discloses,
But they fall silently like dew on Roses.

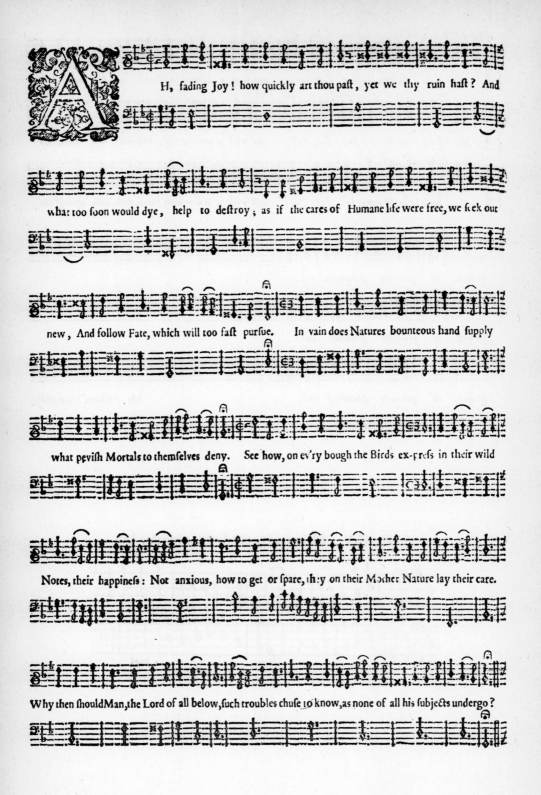

H, fading Joy! how quickly art thou past, yet we thy ruin hast? And

what too soon would dye, help to destroy; as if the cares of Humane life were free, we seek out

new, And follow Fate, which will too fast pursue.   In vain does Natures bounteous hand supply

what pevish Mortals to themselves deny.   See how, on ev'ry bough the Birds ex-press in their wild

Notes, their happiness: Not anxious, how to get or spare, they on their Mother Nature lay their care.

Why then shouldMan, the Lord of all below, such troubles chuse to know, as none of all his subjects undergo?

CHORUS a. 3. Voc.

Hark! hark! the Waters fall, fall, fall; and with a murmuring sound, dash, dash, against the

Hark! hark! the Waters fall, fall, fall; and with a murmuring sound, dash, dash, against the

Hark! hark! the Waters fall, fall, fall; and with a murmuring sound, dash, dash, against the

ground, to gen---tle Slumbers call.

ground, to gen---tle Slumbers call.

ground, to gen---tle Slumbers call.

Mr. *Pelham Humphry*.

Song V. [*Choice Ayres, Songs, & Dialogues*, 1675, I, 70–71]

AIR XLV. Make ready, fair Lady, to-night, &c.

Song VII. [*The Village Opera*, 1729, Air XLV]

3

Thus to prevent my love from being cruel,
My heart's the sacrifice as 'tis the fuel:
And while I suffer this to give him quiet,
My faith rewards my love, though he deny it.

4

On his eyes will I gaze, and there delight me;
While I conceal my love, no frown can fright me:
To be more happy I dare not aspire;
Nor can I fall more low, mounting no higher.

[*Secret-Love*, 1668, ACT IV]

VII

I

Make ready fair Lady to night,
  And stand at the Door below,
For I will be there
To receive you with care,
  And to your true Love you shall go.

2

And when the Stars twinckle so bright,
  Then down to the Door will I creep,
To my Love will I flye,
E're the jealous can spye,
  And leave my old daddy asleep.

[*Sir Martin Mar-all*, 1668, ACT IV]

VIII

The *SONG*.

I

Blind Love to this hour
Had never like me, a slave under his power.
Then blest be the Dart
That he threw at my heart,
For nothing can prove
A joy so great as to be wounded with love.

2

My Days and my Nights
Are fill'd to the purpose with sorrows and frights;
From my heart still I sigh
And my Eyes are ne're dry,
So that *Cupid* be prais'd,
I am to the top of Love's happiness rais'd.

3

My Soul's all on fire,
So that I have the pleasure to doat and desire,
Such a pretty soft pain
That it tickles each vein;
'Tis the dream of a smart,
Which makes me breathe short when it beats at my heart.

4

Sometimes in a Pet,
When I am despis'd, I my freedom would get;
But streight a sweet smile
Does my anger beguile,
And my heart does recall,
Then the more I do struggle, the lower I fall.

5

Heaven does not impart
Such a grace as to love unto ev'ry ones heart;
For many may wish
To be wounded and miss:
Then blest be loves Fire,
And more blest her Eyes that first taught me desire.

[*Sir Martin Mar-all*, 1668, ACT V]

IX

A Dialogue within sung in parts.

1

1D. Where does proud Ambition dwell?
2. In the lowest Rooms of Hell.
1. Of the damn'd who leads the Host?
2. He who did oppress the most.
1. Who such Troops of damned brings?

2.   Most are led by fighting Kings.
     Kings who did Crowns unjustly get,
     Here on burning Thrones are set.
Chor.   Kings who did Crowns, &c.

2

1.   Who are the Pillars of Ambitions Court?
2.   Grim Deaths and Scarlet Murthers it support.
1.   What lyes beneath her feet?
2.   Her footsteps tread,
     On Orphans tender breasts, and Brothers dead.
1.   Can Heaven permit such Crimes should be
     Rewarded with felicity?
2.   Oh no! uneasily their Crowns they wear,
     And their own guilt amidst their Guards they fear.
     Cares when they wake their minds unquiet keep,
     And we in visions lord it o're their sleep.
Cho.   Oh no! uneasily their Crowns, &c.

[*The Tempest*, 1670, ACT II]

X

Around, around, we pace
About this cursed place,
Whilst thus we compass in
These mortals and their sin.

[*The Tempest*, 1670, ACT II]

XI

Dry those eyes which are o'reflowing,
All your storms are over-blowing:
While you in this Isle are bideing,
You shall feast without providing:
Every dainty you can think of,
Ev'ry Wine which you would drink of,
Shall be yours; all want shall shun you,
Ceres blessing so is on you.

[*The Tempest*, 1670, ACT III]

XII

Ferdinand.   Go thy way.
Ariel.   Go thy way.
Ferd.   Why should'st thou stay?
Ariel.   Why should'st thou stay?
Ferd. Where the Winds whistle, and where the streams
                    creep,
          Under yond Willow-tree, fain would I sleep.
                    Then let me alone,
                    For 'tis time to be gone.
Ariel.   For 'tis time to be gone.
Ferd. What cares or pleasures can be in this Isle?
               Within this desart place
               There lives no humane race;
     Fate cannot frown here, nor kind fortune smile.

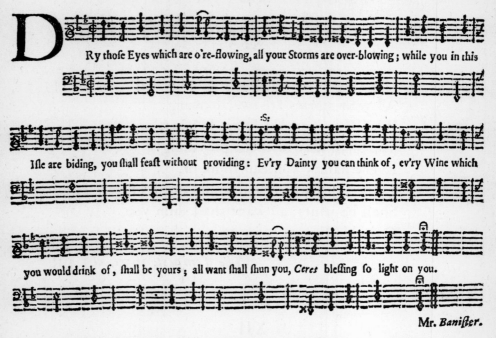

DRy thofe Eyes which are o're-flowing, all your Storms are over-blowing; while you in this

Ifle are biding, you fhall feaft without providing: Ev'ry Dainty you can think of, ev'ry Wine which

you would drink of, fhall be yours; all want fhall fhun you, *Ceres* bleffing fo light on you.

Mr. Banifter.

Song XI. [*The Ariel's Songs in the Play Call'd the Tempest, ca. 1675, No. 2*]

ECCHO Song, 'twixt Ferdinand and Ariel.

Ariel. Go thy way, why should'st thou stay,

Ferdinand. Go thy way, why should'st thou stay, where the Winds

Ariel. where the Winds whistle, and where the Streams creep? Under yonder

Ferdinand. whistle, and where the Streams creep? Under yonder Willow Tree fain would I

Ariel. Willow Tree fain would I Sleep. Then let me alone, for 'tis time to be gone:

Ferdinand. Sleep. Then let me alone, for 'tis time to be gone.

Ariel. What Cares and Pleasures can be in this Isle? Within this

Ferdinand. What Cares and Pleasures can be in this Isle? Within this Desart place there

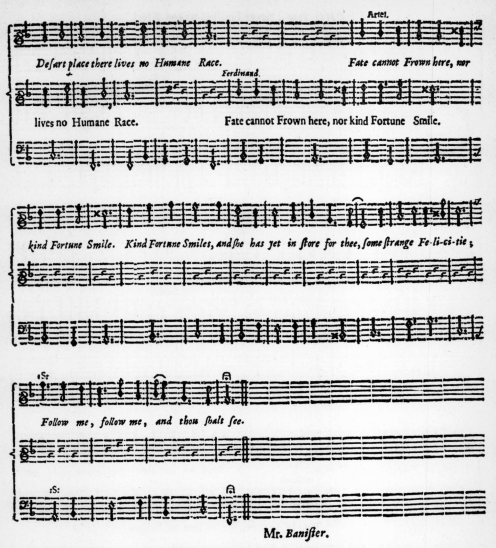

Desart place there lives no Humane Race.   *Fate cannot Frown here, nor*

Ferdinand.

lives no Humane Race.   *Fate cannot Frown here, nor kind Fortune Smile.*

kind Fortune Smile. Kind Fortune Smiles, and she has yet in store for thee, some strange Fe-li-ci-tie;

Follow me, follow me, and thou shalt see.

Mr. Banister.

Song XII. [*The Ariel's Songs in the Play Call'd the Tempest, ca.* 1675, No. 3]

Ariel. Kind Fortune smiles, and she
　　　Has yet in store for thee
　　　Some strange felicity.
　　　Follow me, follow me,
　　　And thou shalt see.

　　　　　　　　　[*The Tempest*, 1670, ACT III]

XIII

We want Musick, we want Mirth,
Up Dam and cleave the Earth,
We have now no Lords that wrong us,
Send thy merry Sprights among us.

　　　　　　　　　[*The Tempest*, 1670, ACT IV]

XIV

Nakar.　Hark, my *Damilcar*, we are call'd below!
Dam.　　Let us go, let us go!
　　　　Go to relieve the care
　　　　Of longing Lovers in despair!
Nakar.　Merry, merry, merry, we sail from the East
　　　　Half tippled at a Rain-bow Feast.
Dam.　　In the bright Moon-shine while winds whistle
　　　　　loud,
　　　　Tivy, tivy, tivy, we mount and we fly,
　　　　All racking along in a downy white Cloud:
　　　　And lest our leap from the Skie should prove too
　　　　　far,

We slide on the back of a new-falling Star.

Nakar.   And drop from above,
In a Gelly of Love!

Dam.   But now the Sun's down, and the Element's red,
The Spirits of Fire against us make head!

Nakar.   They muster, they muster, like Gnats in the Air:
Alas! I must leave thee, my Fair;
And to my light Horse-men repair.

Dam.   O stay, for you need not to fear 'em to night;
The wind is for us, and blows full in their sight:
And o're the wide Ocean we fight!
Like leaves in the Autumn our Foes will fall
down;
And hiss in the Water - - - -

Both.   And hiss in the Water and drown!

Nakar.   But their men lye securely intrench'd in a Cloud:
And a Trumpeter-Hornet to battel sounds loud.

Dam.   Now Mortals that spie
How we tilt in the Skie
With wonder will gaze;
And fear such events as will ne're come to pass!

Nakar.   Stay you to perform what the man will have
done.

Dam.   Then call me again when the Battel is won.

Both.   So ready and quick is a Spirit of Air
To pity the Lover, and succour the fair,
That, silent and swift, the little soft God
Is here with a wish, and is gone with a nod.

[*Tyrannick Love*, 1670, ACT IV]

Song by spirits in Tyranick love or the Royall Martyr

Hark hark my Damilcar wee're call'd below let us goe let us goe to

releive the care of longing louers in disspair''   merry merry merry

wee sayle from the East halfe rippled att the Rainebow feast in the

bright Moonshine when the winds whistle loud Tivy tivy tivy tivy

wee'l Mount and wee'l fly all rocking along in a downy white Cloud

and least our leage from the Sky should proue to far wee'l slide on

the back of a new falling Star and drop from aboue in a Jelly of loue

but now the suns down and the Ellements red   the spirits of

fire against vs made head they muster they muster like gnats in

the Air and alas I must leaue thee my dear and to my light

horseman repair   o stay for you need not to fear them to night

the wind is for us and blows full in their sight and ore the wide

Song XIV. [British Museum: Addit. MS. 19759, ff. 29ᵛ–30]

XV

You pleasing dreams of Love and sweet delight,
Appear before this slumbring Virgins sight:
Soft visions set her free
From mournful piety.
Let her sad thoughts from Heav'n retire;
And let the Melancholy Love
Of those remoter joys above
Give place to your more sprightly fire.
Let purling streams be in her fancy seen;
And flowry Meads, and Vales of chearful green:
And in the midst of deathless Groves
Soft sighing wishes ly,
And smiling hopes fast by,
And just beyond 'em ever laughing Loves.

[*Tyrannick Love*, 1670, ACT IV]

XVI

SONG.

I

Ah how sweet it is to love,
Ah how gay is young desire!
And what pleasing pains we prove
When we first approach Loves fire!
  Pains of Love be sweeter far
  Than all other pleasures are.

2

Sighs which are from Lovers blown,
Do but gently heave the Heart:
Ev'n the tears they shed alone
Cure, like trickling Balm their smart.
  Lovers when they lose their breath,
  Bleed away in easie death.

3

Love and Time with reverence use,
Treat 'em like a parting friend:
Nor the golden gifts refuse
Which in youth sincere they send:
  For each year their price is more,
  And they less simple than before.

4

Love, like Spring-tides full and high,
Swells in every youthful vein:
But each Tide does less supply,
Till they quite shrink in again:
  If a flow in Age appear,
  'Tis but rain, and runs not clear.

[*Tyrannick Love*, 1670, ACT IV]

XVII

SONG.

I

You charm'd me not with that fair face
  Though it was all divine:
To be anothers is the Grace,
  That makes me wish you mine.

2

The Gods and Fortune take their part
  Who like young Monarchs fight;
And boldly dare invade that heart
  Which is anothers right.

3

First mad with hope we undertake
  To pull up every barr;
But once possess'd, we faintly make
  A dull defensive warr.

4

Now every friend is turn'd a foe
  In hope to get our store:
And passion makes us Cowards grow,
  Which made us brave before.

[*An Evening's Love*, 1671, ACT II]

XVIII

SONG.

1

After the pangs of a desperate Lover,
When day and night I have sigh'd all in vain,
Ah what a pleasure it is to discover
In her eyes pity, who causes my pain!

2

When with unkindness our love at a stand is,
And both have punish'd our selves with the pain,
Ah what a pleasure the touch of her hand is,
Ah what a pleasure to press it again!

3

When the denyal comes fainter and fainter,
And her eyes give what her tongue does deny,
Ah what a trembling I feel when I venture,
Ah what a trembling does usher my joy!

4

When, with a Sigh, she accords me the blessing,
And her eyes twinkle 'twixt pleasure and pain;
Ah what a joy 'tis beyond all expressing,
Ah what a joy to hear, shall we again?

[*An Evening's Love*, 1671, ACT II]

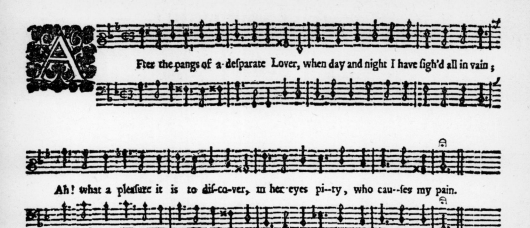

Fter the pangs of a desparate Lover, when day and night I have sigh'd all in vain;

Ah! what a pleasure it is to dif-co-ver, in her eyes pi--ty, who cau--fes my pain.

Mr. *Alph. Marfh.*

I.	II.
When with unkindnefs our Love at a ftand is,	When the denyal comes fainter and fainter,
And both have punifh'd our felves with the pain;	And her Eyes give what her Tongue does deny
Ah, what a pleafure the touch of her hand is!	Ah, what a trembling I feel when I venture!
Ah, what a pleafure to prefs it again!	Ah, what a trembling does ufher my Joy!

III.

When with a figh, fhe accords me the bleffing,
And her Eyes twinkle 'twixt pleafure and pain:
Ah, what a Joy 'tis beyond all expreffing!
Ah! what a Joy to hear, fhall we again?

Song XVIII. [*Choice Songs and Ayres*, 1673, p. 8]

XIX

SONG.

I

Calm was the Even, and cleer was the Skie,
   And the new budding flowers did spring,
When all alone went *Amyntas* and I
   To hear the sweet Nightingale sing;
I sate, and he laid him down by me;
   But scarcely his breath he could draw;
For when with a fear he began to draw near,
   He was dash'd with A ha ha ha ha!

2

He blush'd to himself, and lay still for a while,
   And his modesty curb'd his desire;
But streight I convinc'd all his fear with a smile,
   Which added new flames to his fire.
O *Sylvia*, said he, you are cruel,
   To keep your poor Lover in awe;
Then once more he prest with his hand to my brest,
   But was dash'd with A ha ha ha ha.

3

I knew 'twas his passion that caus'd all his fear;
   And therefore I pity'd his case:
I whisper'd him softly there's no body near,
   And layd my cheek close to his face:

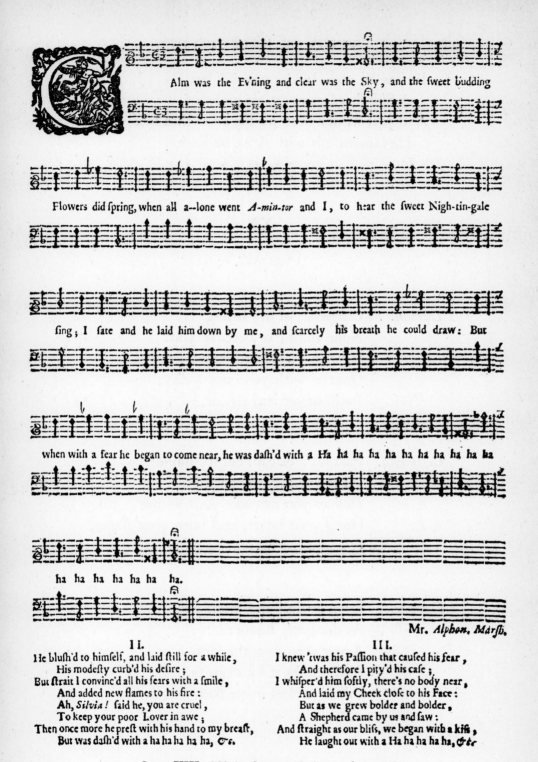

CAlm was the Ev'ning and clear was the Sky, and the sweet budding Flowers did spring, when all a--lone went *A-min-tor* and I, to hear the sweet Nigh-tin-gale sing; I sate and he laid him down by me, and scarcely his breath he could draw: But when with a fear he began to come near, he was dash'd with a Ha ha ha ha ha ha ha ha ha ha ha ha ha ha ha ha ha ha.

Mr. *Alphon. Marsh.*

II.
He blush'd to himself, and laid still for a while,
His modesty curb'd his desire ;
But strait I convinc'd all his fears with a smile,
And added new flames to his fire :
Ah, *Silvia!* said he, you are cruel,
To keep your poor Lover in awe ;
Then once more he prest with his hand to my breast,
But was dash'd with a ha ha ha ha ha, &c.

III.
I knew 'twas his Passion that caused his fear,
And therefore I pity'd his case ;
I whisper'd him softly, there's no body near,
And laid my Cheek close to his Face :
But as we grew bolder and bolder,
A Shepherd came by us and saw :
And straight as our bliss, we began with a kiss,
He laught out with a Ha ha ha ha ha, &c.

SONG XIX. [*Choice Songs and Ayres*, 1673, p. 9]

But as he grew bolder and bolder,
  A Shepherd came by us and saw;
And just as our bliss we began with a kiss,
  He laughd out with A ha ha ha ha.

[*An Evening's Love*, 1671, ACT IV]

XX

SONG.

1

Damon. *Celimena*, of my heart,
      None shall e're bereave you:
      If, with your good leave, I may
      Quarrel with you once a day,
      I will never leave you.

2

Celimena. Passion's but an empty name
      Where respect is wanting:
      Damon you mistake your ayme;
      Hang your heart, and burn your flame,
      If you must be ranting.

3

Damon. Love as dull and muddy is,
      As decaying liquor:
      Anger sets it on the lees,
      And refines it by degrees,
      Till it workes it quicker.

4

Celimena.   Love by quarrels to beget
           Wisely you endeavour;
           With a grave Physician's wit
           Who to cure an Ague fit
           Put me in a Feavor.

5

Damon.   Anger rouzes love to fight,
           And his only bayt is,
           'Tis the spurre to dull delight,
           And is but an eager bite,
           When desire at height is.

6

Celimena.   If such drops of heat can fall
           In our wooing weather;
           If such drops of heat can fall,
           We shall have the Devil and all
           When we come together.

              [*An Evening's Love*, 1671, ACT V]

XXI

SONG.

I

Beneath a Myrtle shade
Which Love for none but happy Lovers made,
I slept, and straight my Love before me brought
Phillis the object of my waking thought;
Undress'd she came my flames to meet,
While Love strow'd flow'rs beneath her feet;
Flow'rs, which so press'd by her, became more sweet.

2

From the bright Visions head
A careless vail of Lawn was loosely spread:
From her white temples fell her shaded hair,
Like cloudy sunshine not too brown nor fair:
Her hands, her lips did love inspire;
Her every grace my heart did fire:
But most her eyes which languish'd with desire.

3

Ah, Charming fair, said I,
How long can you my bliss and yours deny?
By Nature and by love this lonely shade
Was for revenge of suffring Lovers made:
Silence and shades with love agree:
Both shelter you and favour me;
You cannot blush because I cannot see.

Beneath a Mirtle shade, which Love for none but happy Lovers made;

I slept, and streight my Love before me brought, *Phillis*, the Object of my waking thought:

Undrest she comes, my flames to meet; whilst Love straw'd flow'rs beneath her Feet, so prest by

her, became, became more sweet.

Mr. *John Banister.*

II.
From the bright Visions head,
A careless vail of Lawn was loosly spread;
From her white Temples fell her shaded Hair,
Like cloudy Sun-shine, not too brown or fair:
Her Hands, her Lips, did Love inspire,
Her ev'ry Grace my Heart did fire;
But most her Eyes, that languish'd with desire.

III.
Ah, charming Fair, said I,
How long can you my bliss and yours deny:
By Nature and by Love this lovely shade
Was for revenge of suff'ring Lovers made.
Silence and shades with Love agree,
Both shelter you, and favour me;
You cannot blush, because I cannot see.

IV.
No, let me dye, she said,
Rather than lose the spotless name of Maid;
Faintly she spoke, methought, for all the while
She bid me not believe her, with a smile.
Then dye, said I, she still deny'd,
And is it thus? Thus, thus, she cry'd,
You use a harmless maid, and so she dy'd.

V.
I wak't, and straight I knew
I lov'd so well, it made my dream prove true:
Fancy the kinder Mistress of the two,
Fancy had done what *Phillis* would not do.
Ah, cruel Nymph, cease your disdain,
While I can dream you scorn in vain,
Asleep, or waking, you must ease my pain.

SONG XXI. [*Choice Songs and Ayres*, 1673, p. 45]

4

No, let me dye, she said,
Rather than lose the spotless name of Maid:
Faintly me thought she spoke, for all the while
She bid me not believe her, with a smile.
Then dye, said I, she still deny'd:
And, is it thus, thus, thus she cry'd
You use a harmless Maid, and so she dy'd!

5

I wak'd, and straight I knew
I lov'd so well it made my dream prove true:
Fancy, the kinder Mistress of the two,
Fancy had done what *Phillis* wou'd not do!
Ah, Cruel Nymph, cease your disdain,
While I can dream you scorn in vain;
Asleep or waking you must ease my pain.

[*The Conquest of Granada*, 1672, ACT III]

XXII

SONG.

I

Wherever I am, and whatever I doe;
My *Phillis* is still in my mind:
When angry I mean not to *Phillis* to goe,
My Feet of themselves the way find:
Unknown to my self I am just at her door,
And when I would raile, I can bring out no more,
Than *Phillis* too fair and unkind!

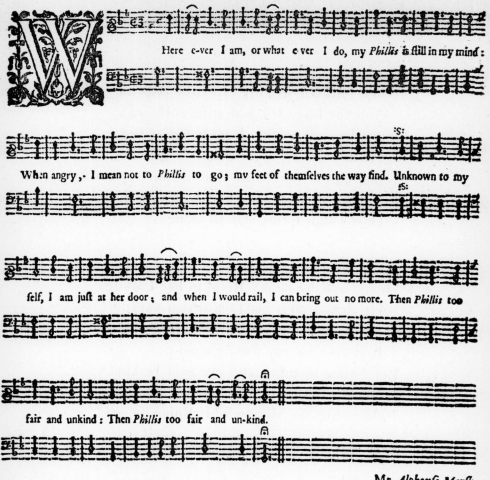

Here e-ver I am, or what e-ver I do, my *Phillis* is still in my mind:

When angry,- I mean not to *Phillis* to go; mv feet of themselves the way find. Unknown to my

self, I am juft at her door; and when I would rail, I can bring out no more. Then *Phillis* too

fair and unkind: Then *Phillis* too fair and un-kind.

Mr. *Alphonfo Marfh.*

II.

When *Phillis* I fee, my heart burns in my breaft,
And the Love I would ftifle is fhow'n:
But afleep or awake, I am never at reft,
When from mine eyes *Phillis* is gone.
Somitimes a fweet dream doth delude my fad mind;
But alafs! when I wake, and no *Phillis* I find,
Then I figh to my felf all alone!
Then I figh to my felf all alone!

III.

Should a King be my rival in her I adore,
He fhould offer his treafure in vain:
O let me alone to be happy and poor,
And give me my *Phillis* again.
Let *Phillis* be mine, and ever be kind,
I could to a Defart with her be confin'd;
And envy no Monarch his reign:
And envy no Monarch his reign.

IV.

Alafs! I difcover too much of my Love;
And fhe too well knows her own pow'r:
She makes me each day a new Martyrdom prove,
And makes me grow jealous each hour.
But let her each minute torment my poor mind,
I had rather love *Phillis*, both falfe and unkind,
Then ever be freed from her pow'r:
Then ever be freed from her pow'r.

SONG XXII. [*Choice Songs and Ayres*, 1673, p. 37]

2

When *Phillis* I see, my Heart bounds in my Breast,
  And the Love I would stifle is shown:
But asleep, or awake, I am never at rest
  When from my Eyes *Phillis* is gone!
Sometimes a sad Dream does delude my sad mind,
But, alas, when I wake and no *Phillis* I find
  How I sigh to my self all alone.

3

Should a King be my Rival in her I adore
  He should offer his Treasure in vain:
O let me alone to be happy and poor,
  And give me my *Phillis* again:
Let *Phillis* be mine, and but ever be kind
I could to a Desart with her be confin'd,
  And envy no Monarch his Raign.

4

Alas, I discover too much of my Love,
  And she too well knows her own power!
She makes me each day a new Martyrdom prove,
  And makes me grow jealous each hour:
But let her each minute torment my poor mind
I had rather love *Phillis* both False and Unkind,
  Than ever be freed from her Pow'r.

[*The Conquest of Granada*, 1672, ACT IV]

XXIII

Song, In two Parts.

I

He.   How unhappy a Lover am I
      While I sigh for my *Phillis* in vain;
    All my hopes of Delight
    Are another man's Right,
      Who is happy while I am in pain!

2

She.   Since her Honour allows no Relief,
      But to pity the pains which you bear,
    'Tis the best of your Fate,
    (In a hopeless Estate,)
      To give o're, and betimes to despair.

3

He.   I have try'd the false Med'cine in vain;
      For I wish what I hope not to win:
    From without, my desire
    Has no Food to its Fire,
      But it burns and consumes me within.

4

She.   Yet at least 'tis a pleasure to know
      That you are not unhappy alone:
    For the Nymph you adore
    Is as wretched and more,
      And accounts all your suff'rings her own.

5

He.   O ye Gods, let me suffer for both;
       At the feet of my *Phillis* I'le lye:
      I'le resign up my Breath,
      And take pleasure in Death,
        To be pity'd by her when I dye.

6

She.   What her Honour deny'd you in Life
       In her Death she will give to your Love.
      Such a Flame as is true
      After Fate will renew,
        For the Souls to meet closer above.

[*Almanzor and Almahide*, 1672, ACT IV]

XXIV

A SONG.

I

Farewel, fair *Armeda*, my Joy and my Grief;
In vain I have Lov'd you, and find no Relief:
Undone by your Vertue, too strict and severe,
Your Eyes gave me Love, and you gave me Despair.
Now, call'd by my Honour, I seek, with Content,
A Fate which in pity you wou'd not prevent:
    To languish in Love, were to find by delay
    A Death, that's more welcom the speediest way.

How unhappy a Lover am I, whilst I sigh for my *Phillis* in vain: All my hopes of delight are another man's right; who is happy, whilst I am in pain. Since her honour affords no re-lief; but to pi-ty the pains which you bear: Tis the best of your fate in a hopeless e-state, to give o're, and betimes to des-pair.

Mr. *Nicholas Staggins.*

II.

I have try'd the false Medicine in vain;
Yet I wish what I hope not to win:
From without my desire has no food to its fire,
But it burns and consumes me within.
Yet at least, 'tis a comfort to know
That you are not unhappy alone:
For the Nimph you adore is as wretched or more,
And accounts all your suff'rings her own.

III.

O you pow'rs! let me suffer for both;
At the feet of my *Phillis* I'le lye:
I'le resign up my breath, and take pleasure in death,
To be pity'd by her when I dye.
What her honour deny'd you in life,
In her death she will give to her love:
Such a flame as is true, after fate will renew,
When the souls do meet closer above.

SONG XXIII. [*Choice Songs and Ayres*, 1673, p. 38]

2

On Seas, and in Battels, in Bullets and Fire,
The Danger is less than in Hopeless Desire.
My Deaths Wound you gave me, though far off I bear
My Fate from your sight, not to cost you a Tear.
But if the kind Flood on a Wave should convey,
And under your Window my Body should lay,
The Wound on my Breast when you happen to see,
You'll say with a Sigh, — *It was given by me.*

[*New Court-Songs*, 1672]

XXV

1

Why should a foolish Marriage Vow
    Which long ago was made,
Oblige us to each other now
    When Passion is decay'd?
We lov'd, and we lov'd, as long as we cou'd,
    Till our love was lov'd out in us both:
But our Marriage is dead, when the Pleasure is fled:
    'Twas Pleasure first made it an Oath.

2

If I have Pleasures for a Friend,
    And farther love in store,
What wrong has he whose joys did end,
    And who cou'd give no more?

Farewel fair *Armida* my Joy and my Grief, in vain I have Lov'd you, and hope no re-lief: Undone by your Virtue too strict and severe; Your Eyes gave me Love, and you gave me despair. Now call'd by my Honour, I seek with content, the Fate which in pi--ty you would not prevent: To Languish in Love, were to find by de-lay a Death that's more welcome the speedier way.

Mr. *Robert Smith.*

II.

On Seas and in Battles, in Bullets and Fire,
The danger is less then in hopeless desire:
My Deaths wound you gave me though far off I bear,
My Fate from your sight not to cost you a Tear.

III.

But if the kind Floods on a Wave would convey,
And under your Window my Body would lay:
The Wound on my Breast, when you happen to see,
You'l say with a sigh, it was given by me.

SONG XXIV. [*Choice Songs and Ayres*, 1673, p. 10]

'Tis a madness that he
Should be jealous of me,
Or that I shou'd bar him of another:
For all we can gain,
Is to give our selves pain,
When neither can hinder the other.

[*Marriage A-la-Mode*, 1673, ACT I]

XXVI

SONG.

I

Whil'st *Alexis* lay prest
In her Arms he lov'd best,
With his hands round her neck,
And his head on her breast,
He found the fierce pleasure too hasty to stay,
And his soul in the tempest just flying away.

2

When *Cælia* saw this,
With a sigh, and a kiss,
She cry'd, Oh my dear, I am robb'd of my bliss;
'Tis unkind to your Love, and unfaithfully done,
To leave me behind you, and die all alone.

Hy should a foolish Marriage Vow, which long agoe was made, oblige us to each other now, when passion is de-cay'd? We loved and lov'd, as long as we could, 'till our Love was lov'd out of us both. But the Marriage is dead, when the pleasure is fled; 'twas pleasure first made it an Oath.

Mr. *Robert Smith.*

II.

If I have pleasure for a friend,
And further joy in store,
What wrong has he whose joys did end,
And who could give no more?
It's a madness that he
Should be jealous of me,
Or that I should bar him of another;
When all we can gain
Is to give our selves pain,
And neither can hinder the other.

Song XXV. [*Choice Songs and Ayres*, 1673, p. 39]

3

The Youth, though in haste,
And breathing his last,
In pity dy'd slowly, while she dy'd more fast;
Till at length she cry'd, Now, my dear, now let us go,
Now die, my *Alexis*, and I will die too.

4

Thus intranc'd they did lie,
Till *Alexis* did try
To recover new breath, that again he might die:
Then often they di'd; but the more they did so,
The Nymph di'd more quick, and the Shepherd more
    slow.

[*Marriage A-la-Mode*, 1673, ACT IV]

XXVII

Eveillez vous, Belles endormies;
Eveillez vous: car il est jour:
Mettez la tete a la fenestre
Vous entendrez parler d'amour.

[*The Assignation*, 1673, ACT II]

Hilst *A-lex-is* lay preſt in her Arms he Lov'd beſt, with his hand round her

neck, and his head on her breaſt: He found the fierce pleaſure too haſty to ſtay, and his ſoul in a

Tempeſt juſt flying a--way.

Mr. *Nicholas Staggins*.

II.

When *Cælia* ſaw this, with a Sigh and a Kiſs,
She cry'd, O my Dear! I'm robb'd of my bliſs:
'Tis unkind to your Love, and unfaithfully done,
To leave me behind you, and dye all alone.

III.

The Youth, though in haſt, and breathing his laſt,
In pity, dy'd ſlowly, whilſt She dy'd more faſt;
'Till at length ſhe cry'd, now, my Dear, now
Let's go; Now dye, my *Alexis*, and I will dye too.

IV.

Thus intranc'd ſhe did lye, while *Alexis* did try
To recover new breath, that again he might dye:
Then often they dy'd; but the more they did ſo,
The Nimph dy'd more quick, and the Shepherd more ſlow.

SONG XXVI. [*Choice Songs and Ayres*, 1673, p. 27]

XXVIII

SONG and DANCE.

I

Long betwixt Love and fear *Phillis* tormented,
Shun'd her own wish yet at last she consented:
But loath that day shou'd her blushes discover,
　Come gentle Night She said,
　Come quickly to my aid,
　And a poor Shamefac'd Maid
　Hide from her Lover.

2

Now cold as Ice I am, now hot as Fire,
I dare not tell my self my own desire;
But let Day fly away, and let Night hast her:
　Grant yee kind Powers above,
　Slow houres to parting Love,
　But when to Bliss we move,
　Bid 'em fly faster.

3

How sweet it is to Love when I discover,
That Fire which burns my Heart, warming my Lover;
'Tis pitty Love so true should be mistaken:
　But if this Night he be
　False or unkinde to me,
　Let me dye ere I see
　That I'me forsaken.

[*The Assignation*, 1673, ACT III]

LOng betwixt hope and fear, *Phillis* tormented, fhun'd her own wifh, yet at laft fhe confented: But loath that day fhould her blufhes dif-co-ver; Come gentle night, fhe faid, Come quickly to my aid; And a poor fhame-fac'd Maid hide from her Lover.

Mr. *Robert Smith.*

II.

Now cold as Ice I am, now hot as Fire ;
I dare not tell my felf my own defire :
But let day fly away, and bid night haft her ;
Grant ye kind pow'rs above
Slow hours to parting Love :
But whom to blifs we move, let them fly fafter.

III.

How fweet it is to Love, when I difcover
Thofe Flames that burn my Soul, warming my Lover
'Tis pity Love fo true, fhould be miftaken ;
If that this night he be
Falfe, or unkind to me :
Let me dye, e're I fee, That I'm forfaken.

Song XXVIII. [*Choice Songs and Ayres*, 1673, p. 59]

XXIX

Epithalamium.

1

The day is come, I see it rise,
Betwixt the Bride's and Bridegroom's Eyes,
That Golden day they wish'd so long,
Love pick'd it out amidst the throng;
He destin'd to himself this Sun,
And took the Reins and drove him on;
In his own Beams he drest him bright,
Yet bid him bring a better night.

2

The day you wish'd arriv'd at last,
You wish as much that it were past,
One Minute more and night will hide,
The Bridegroom and the blushing Bride.
The Virgin now to Bed do's goe:
Take care oh Youth, she rise not soe;
She pants and trembles at her doom,
And fears and wishes thou wou'dst come.

3

The Bridegroom comes, He comes apace
With Love and Fury in his Face;
She shrinks away, He close pursues,
And Prayers and Threats, at once do's use,

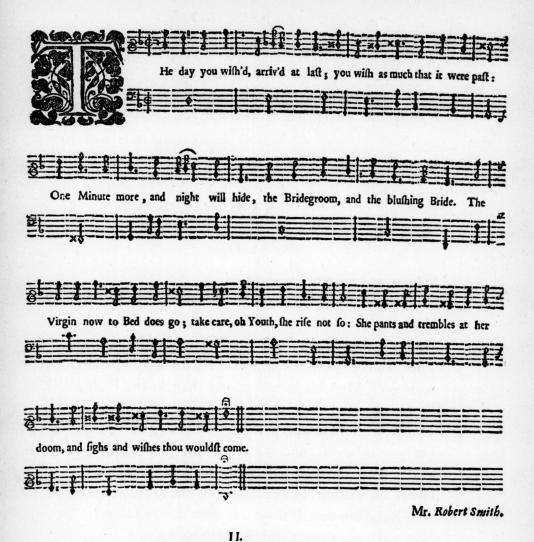

He day you wish'd, arriv'd at last; you wish as much that it were past:

One Minute more, and night will hide, the Bridegroom, and the blushing Bride. The

Virgin now to Bed does go; take care, oh Youth, she rise not so: She pants and trembles at her

doom, and sighs and wishes thou wouldst come.

Mr. *Robert Smith.*

II.
The Bridegroom comes, he comes apace,
With Love and Fury in his Face;
She shrinks away, he close pursues,
And Prayers and Threats at once does use:
She softly sighing, begs delay,
And with her hand puts his away:
Now out aloud for help she cryes,
And now despairing shuts her Eyes.

Song XXIX. [*Choice Songs and Ayres*, 1673, p. 60]

She softly sighing begs delay,
And with her hand puts his away,
Now out aloud for help she cryes,
And now despairing shuts her Eyes.

[*Amboyna*, 1673, ACT III]

XXX

The Sea Fight.

Who ever saw a noble sight,
That never view'd a brave Sea Fight:
Hang up your bloody Colours in the Aire,
Up with your Fights and your Nettings prepare,
Your Merry Mates chear, with a lusty bold spright,
Now each Man his brindice, and then to the Fight,
St. George, *St. George* we cry,
The shouting Turks reply.
Oh now it begins, and the Gunroom grows hot,
Plie it with Culverin and with small shot;
Heark do's it not Thunder, no 'tis the Guns roar,
The Neighbouring Billows are turn'd into Gore,
Now each man must resolve to dye,
For here the Coward cannot flye.
Drums and Trumpets toll the Knell,
And Culverins the Passing Bell.
Now now they Grapple, and now board a Main,
Blow up the Hatches, they're off all again:
Give 'em a broadside, the Dice run at all,

Down comes the Mast and Yard, and tacklings fall,
She grows giddy now like blind fortunes wheel,
She sinks there, she sinks, she turns up her Keel,
Who ever beheld so noble a sight
As this so brave, so bloody Sea Fight.

[*Amboyna*, 1673, ACT III]

XXXI

Angel, singing.   Look up, look up, and see
What Heav'n prepares for thee;
Look up, and this fair fruit behold,
Ruddy it smiles, and rich with streaks of gold.
The loaded branches downward bend,
Willing they stoop, and thy fair hand attend
Fair Mother of Mankind, make haste
And bless, and bless thy senses with the taste.
Woman.   No; tis forbidden, I
In tasting it shall dye.
Angel.   Say who injoyn'd this harsh command.
Woman.   'Twas Heav'n; and who can Heav'n withstand?
Angel.   Why was it made so fair, why plac'd in sight?
Heav'n is too good to envy man's delight.
See, we before thy face will try,
What thou so fear'st and will not dye.
Angels singing.   Behold what a change on a sudden is
here!
How glorious in beauty how bright they appear!
From spirits deform'd they are Deities made

Their pinions at pleasure, the clouds can invade,
Till equal in honor they rise
With him who commands in the skies:
Then taste without fear, and be happy and wise.

Woman.   Ah, now I believe; such a pleasure I find
As enlightens my eyes, and enlivens my mind.
I only repent
I deferr'd my content.

Angel.   Now wiser experience has taught you to prove
What a folly it is,
Out of fear to shun bliss.
To the joy that's forbidden we eagerly move;
It inhances the price, and increases the love.

Chorus of both.   To the joy, &c.

[*The State of Innocence*, 1677, ACT III]

XXXII

SONG to Apollo.

Phœbus, God belov'd by men;
At thy dawn, every Beast is rouz'd in his Den;
At thy setting, all the Birds of thy absence complain,
And we dye, all dye till the morning comes again,
    Phœbus, God belov'd by men!
    Idol of the Eastern Kings,
    Awful as the God who flings
    His Thunder round, and the Lightning wings;
    God of Songs, and *Orphean* strings,

Who to this mortal bosom brings,
All harmonious heav'nly things!
Thy drouzie Prophet to revive,
Ten thousand thousand forms before him drive;
With Chariots and Horses all o' fire awake him,
Convulsions, and Furies, and Prophesies shake him:
Let him tell it in groans, tho' he bend with the load,
Tho' he burst with the weight of the terrible God.

[*Oedipus*, 1679, ACT II]

XXXIII

1

Tir. Chuse the darkest part o' th' Grove;
 Such as Ghosts at noon-day love.
 Dig a Trench, and dig it nigh
 Where the bones of *Lajus* lye.
 Altars rais'd of Turf or Stone,
 Will th' Infernal Pow'rs have none.
 Answer me, if this be done?

All Pr. 'Tis done.

2

Tir. Is the Sacrifice made fit?
 Draw her backward to the pit:
 Draw the barren Heyfer back;
 Barren let her be and black.
 Cut the curled hair that grows
 Full betwixt her horns and brows:

And turn your faces from the Sun:
Answer me, if this be done?

All Pr. 'Tis done.

3

Tir.   Pour in blood, and blood like wine,
To Mother Earth and *Proserpine*:
Mingle Milk into the stream;
Feast the Ghosts that love the steam;
Snatch a brand from funeral pile;
Toss it in to make 'em boil;
And turn your faces from the Sun;
Answer me, if all be done?

All Pr. All is done.

[*Oedipus*, 1679, ACT III]

XXXIV

I

1. Hear, ye sullen Pow'rs below:
      Hear, ye taskers of the dead.
2. You that boiling Cauldrons blow,
      You that scum the molten Lead.
3. You that pinch with Red-hot Tongs;
1.   You that drive the trembling hosts
      Of poor, poor Ghosts,
   With your Sharpen'd Prongs;
2. You that thrust 'em off the Brim.
3. You that plunge 'em when they Swim:

1. Till they drown;
 Till they go
 On a row
 Down, down, down
 Ten thousand thousand, thousand fadoms low.
Chorus. Till they drown, &c.

2

1. Musick for a while
 Shall your cares beguile:
 Wondring how your pains were eas'd.
2. And disdaining to be pleas'd;
3. Till *Alecto* free the dead
 From their eternal bands;
 Till the snakes drop from her head,
 And whip from out her hands.
1. Come away
 Do not stay,
 But obey
 While we play,
 For Hell's broke up, and Ghosts have holy-day.
Chorus. Come away, &c.

3

1. Lajus! *2.* Lajus! *3.* Lajus!
1. Hear! *2.* Hear! *3.* Hear!
Tir. Hear and appear:
 By the Fates that spun thy thread;
Cho. Which are three,
Tir. By the Furies fierce, and dread!
Cho. Which are three,
Tir. By the Judges of the dead!

Cho. Which are three,
　　　Three times three!
Tir. By Hells blew flame:
　　　By the *Stygian* Lake:
　　　And by *Demogorgon's* name,
　　　　At which Ghosts quake,
　　　Hear and appear.

[*Oedipus*, 1679, ACT III]

XXXV

Song.

1

Can life be a blessing,
Or worth the possessing,
Can life be a blessing if love were away?
Ah no! though our love all night keep us waking,
And though he torment us with cares all the day,
Yet he sweetens he sweetens our pains in the taking,
There's an hour at the last, there's an hour to repay.

2

In every possessing,
The ravishing blessing,
In every possessing the fruit of our pain,
Poor lovers forget long ages of anguish,
Whate're they have suffer'd and done to obtain;
'Tis a pleasure, a pleasure to sigh and to languish,
When we hope, when we hope to be happy again.

[*Troilus and Cressida*, 1679, ACT III]

An life be a Blessing, or worth the possessing? can life be a
Blessing, if Love were away? Ah no! though our Love all night keep us wa--king; and
though he tor--ment us with cares all the day, yet he sweetens, he sweetens our
pains with the taking: There's an hour at the last, there's an hour to re--pay.

Mr. *Tho. Farmer.*

In every possessing, the ravishing blessing;
In every possessing the fruit of our pains:
Poor Lovers forget long Ages of Anguish,
What e're they have suffer'd, or done to obtain.
'Tis a pleasure, a pleasure, to sigh and to languish,
When we hope, when we hope to be happy again.

Song XXXV. [*Choice Ayres and Songs*, 1681, III, 3]

XXXVI

A SONG.

I

'Gainst Keepers we petition,
Who wou'd inclose the Common:
'Tis enough to raise Sedition
In the free-born subject Woman.
Because for his gold
I my body have sold,
He thinks I'm a Slave for my life;
He rants, domineers,
He swaggers and swears,
And wou'd keep me as bare as his Wife.

2

'Gainst Keepers we petition, &c.
'Tis honest and fair,
That a Feast I prepare;
But when his dull appetite's o're,
I'le treat with the rest
Some welcomer Ghest,
For the Reck'ning was paid me before.

[*The Kind Keeper*, 1680, ACT I]

XXXVII

I my own Jaylour was; my only Foe,
  Who did my liberty forego;
I was a Pris'ner, cause I wou'd be so.

[*The Kind Keeper*, 1680, ACT II]

XXXVIII

A SONG from the ITALIAN.

By a dismal Cypress lying,
Damon cry'd, all pale and dying,
Kind is Death that ends my pain,
But cruel She I lov'd in vain.
The Mossy Fountains
Murmure my trouble,
And hollow Mountains
My groans redouble:
Every Nymph mourns me,
Thus while I languish;
She only scorns me,
Who caus'd my anguish.
No Love returning me, but all hope denying;
By a dismal Cypress lying,
Like a *Swan*, so sung he dying:
Kind is Death that ends my pain,
But cruel She I lov'd in vain.

[*The Kind Keeper*, 1680, ACT III]

XXXIX

1

Look down, ye bless'd above, look down,
  Behold our weeping Matron's Tears,
  Behold our tender Virgins Fears,
And with success our Armies crown.

2

Look down, ye bless'd above, look down:
  Oh! save us, save us, and our State restore;
  For Pitty, Pitty, Pitty, we implore;
For Pitty, Pitty, Pitty, we implore.

[*The Spanish Fryar*, 1681, ACT I]

XL

A SONG.

1

Farewell ungratefull Traytor,
  Farewell my perjur'd Swain,
Let never injur'd Creature
  Believe a Man again.
The Pleasure of Possessing
Surpasses all Expressing,
But 'tis too short a Blessing,
  And Love too long a Pain.

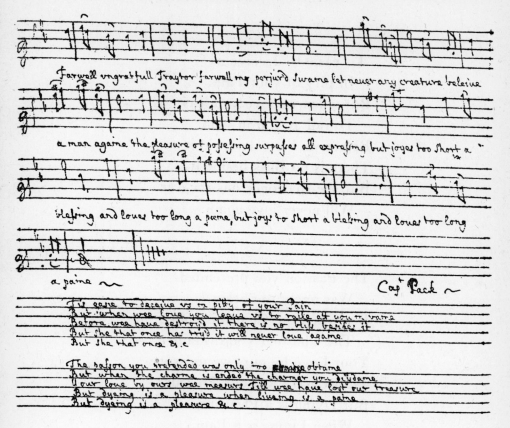

Farwell vngratfull Traytor farwell my perjur'd Swaine let neuer any creature beleiue

a man againe the pleasure of posseßing surpaßes all expreßing but joyes too short a

bleßing and loues too long a paine, but joye to short a bleßing and loues too long

a paine ~

Cap.t Pack ~

Tis easie to deceiue vs in pitty of your Pain
But when wee loue you leaue vs to raile at your vaine
Before wee haue destroy'd it there is no bliß beßides it
But she that once has try'd it will neuer loue againe
But she that once &c

The paßion you pretended was only ~ ——— obtaine
But when the charme is ended the charmer you dißdaine
Your loue vy ours wee measure Till wee haue lost our treasure
But dyeing is a pleasure when liuing is a paine
But dyeing is a pleasure &c

SONG XL. [British Museum: Addit. MS. 19759, f. 20^v]

2

'Tis easie to deceive us
　In pity of your Pain,
But when we love you leave us
　To rail at you in vain.
Before we have descry'd it
There is no Bliss beside it,
But she that once has try'd it
　Will never love again.

3

The Passion you pretended
　Was onely to obtain,
But when the Charm is ended
　The Charmer you disdain.
Your Love by ours we measure
Till we have lost our Treasure,
But Dying is a Pleasure,
　When Living is a Pain.

[*The Spanish Fryar*, 1681, ACT V]

XLI

Malicorn, Malicorn, Malicorn, ho!
If the *Guise* resolves to go,
I charge, I warn thee let him know,
Perhaps his head may lye too low.

[*The Duke of Guise*, 1683, ACT III]

XLII

A Song in the Fifth ACT of the
Duke of GUISE.

I

Shepherdess.

Tell me *Thirsis*, tell your Anguish,
why you Sigh, and why you Languish;
when the Nymph whom you Adore,
grants the Blessing of Possessing,
what can Love and I do more?
what can Love, what can Love and I do
    more?

2

Shepherd.

Think it's Love beyond all measure
makes me faint away with Pleasure
strength of Cordial may destroy,
and the Blessing of Possessing
kills me with excess of Joy.

3

Shepherdess.

Thirsis, how can I believe you?
but confess, and I'le forgive you;
Men are false, and so are you;
never Nature fram'd a Creature
to enjoy, and yet be true;
never Nature fram'd a Creature
to enjoy, and yet be true;
to enjoy, and yet be true,
and yet be true.

A DIALOGUE *betwixt a* Shepherd *and* Shepherdeſs, *ſung in the Play of the* Duke of Guiſe.

A. 2. voc. Cantus & Baſſus.

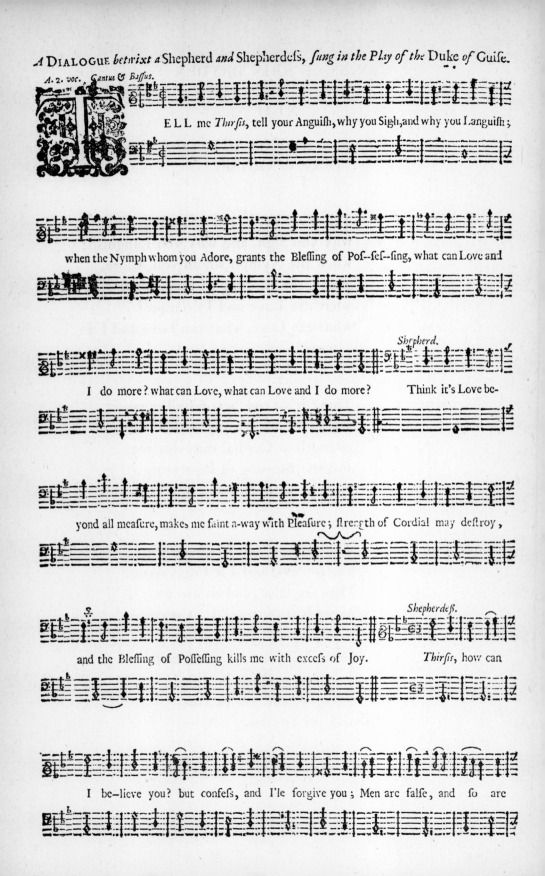

ELL me *Thirſis*, tell your Anguiſh, why you Sigh, and why you Languiſh;

when the Nymph whom you Adore, grants the Bleſſing of Poſ--ſeſ--ſing, what can Love and

I do more? what can Love, what can Love and I do more? Think it's Love be-

yond all meaſure, makes me ſaint a-way with Pleaſure; ſtrength of Cordial may deſtroy,

and the Bleſſing of Poſſeſſing kills me with exceſs of Joy. *Thirſis*, how can

I be-lieve you? but confeſs, and I'le forgive you; Men are falſe, and ſo are

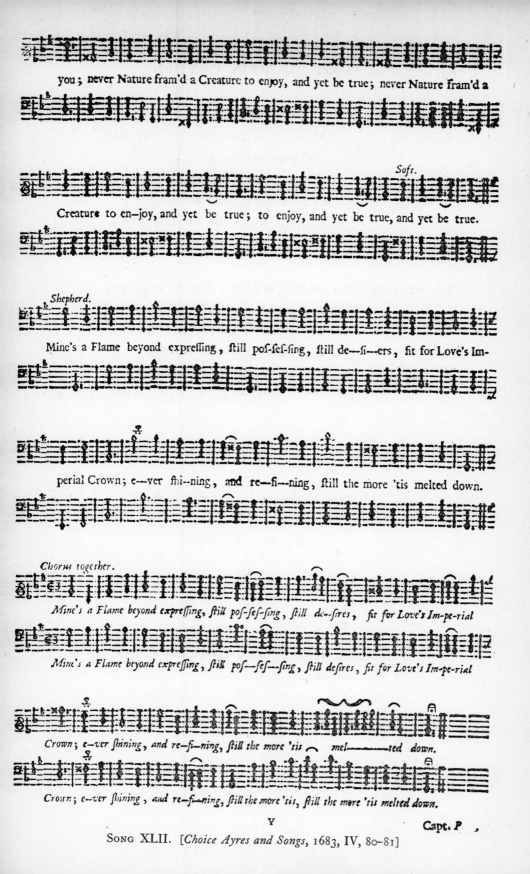

you; never Nature fram'd a Creature to enjoy, and yet be true; never Nature fram'd a

Creature to en—joy, and yet be true; to enjoy, and yet be true, and yet be true.

Soft.

Shepherd.

Mine's a Flame beyond expressing, still pos-ses-sing, still de—si—ers, fit for Love's Im-

perial Crown; e—ver shi—ning, and re—fi—ning, still the more 'tis melted down.

Chorus together.

Mine's a Flame beyond expressing, still pos-ses-sing, still de—sires, fit for Love's Im-pe-rial

Mine's a Flame beyond expressing, still pos—ses—sing, still desires, fit for Love's Im-pe-rial

Crown; e—ver shining, and re—fi—ning, still the more 'tis mel——ted down.

Crown; e—ver shining, and re—fi—ning, still the more 'tis, still the more 'tis melted down.

Y

Capt. *P*

4

Shepherd.   Mine's a Flame beyond expiring,
             still possessing, still desiring,
             fit for Love's Imperial Crown;
             ever shining, and refining,
             still the more 'tis melted down.

5

Chorus together. *Mine's a Flame beyond expiring,*
             still possessing, still desiring,
             fit for Love's Imperial Crown;
             ever shining, and refining,
             still the more 'tis melted down.

[*The Duke of Guise*, 1683, ACT V]

XLIII

The Tears of AMYNTA, for the
Death of DAMON.
By *Mr. Dryden.*

SONG.

I

On a bank, beside a Willow,
Heav'n her Cov'ring, Earth her Pillow,
Sad *Amynta* sigh'd alone:
From the chearless Dawn of Morning
Till the Dew's of Night returning

Singing thus she made her mone:
  Hope is banish'd
  Joys are vanish'd;
Damon, my belov'd is gone!

2

Time, I dare thee to discover
Such a Youth, and such a Lover,
Oh so true, so kind was he!
Damon was the Pride of Nature,
Charming in his every Feature,
Damon liv'd alone for me:
  Melting Kisses
  Murmuring Blisses,
Who so liv'd and lov'd as we!

3

Never shall we curse the Morning,
Never bless the Night returning,
Sweet Embraces to restore:
Never shall we both ly dying
Nature failing, Love supplying
All the Joyes he drain'd before:
  Death, come end me
  To befriend me;
Love and *Damon* are no more.

[*Miscellany Poems*, 1684]

XLIV

Cease, *Augusta*! Cease thy mourning,
Happy dayes appeare,
Godlike *Albion* is returning
Loyal Hearts to Cheere!
Every Grace his youth Adorning,
Glorious as the Star of Morning,
Or the Planet of the Year.

Chor. Godlike *Albion* is returning, *&c.*

[*Albion and Albanius*, 1685, ACT I]

XLV

1

Then Zeal and Common-wealth infest
My Land again;
The fumes of madness that possest
The Peoples giddy Brain,
Once more disturb the Nations rest,
And dye Rebellion in a deeper Stain.

2

Will they at length awake the sleeping Sword,
And force revenge from their offended Lord?
How long, yee Gods, how long
Can Royal patience bear
Th' Insults and wrong
Of Mad-mens jealousies, and causeless fear?

3

I thought their love by mildness might be gain'd,
By Peace I was restor'd, in Peace I Reign'd:
But Tumults, Seditions,
And haughty Petitions,
Are all the effects of a merciful Nature;
Forgiving and granting,
E're Mortals are wanting,
But leads to Rebelling against their Creator.

[*Albion and Albanius*, 1685, ACT II]

XLVI

1

All Hail yee Royal pair!
The God's peculiar care:
Fear not the malice of your Foes;
Their Dark designing
And Combining,
Time and truth shall once expose:
Fear not the malice of your Foes.

2

My sacred Oracles assure,
The Tempest shall not long indure;
But when the Nations Crimes are purg'd away,
Then shall you both in glory shine;
Propitious both, and both Divine:
In Lustre equal to the God of Day.

[*Albion and Albanius*, 1685, ACT II]

XLVII

I

Old Father Ocean calls my Tyde:
Come away, come away;
The Barks upon the Billows ride,
The Master will not stay;
The merry Boson from his side,
His Whistle takes to check and chide
The lingring Lads delay,
And all the Crew alowd has Cry'd,
Come away, come away.

2

See the God of Seas attends Thee,
Nymphs Divine, a Beauteous Train:
All the calmer gales befriend Thee
In thy passage o're the Main:
Every Maid her Locks is binding,
Every *Triton*'s Horn is winding,
Welcome to the watry Plain.

[*Albion and Albanius*, 1685, ACT II]

XLVIII

I

Yee Nymphs, the Charge is Royal,
  Which you must convey;
Your Hearts and Hands employ all,
  Hasten to obey;

When Earth is grown disloyal,
Shew there's Honour in the Sea.

2

Sports and Pleasures shall attend you
  Through all the Watry Plains,
    Where *Neptune* Reigns:
Venus ready to defend you,
  And her Nymphs to ease your Pains.
    No storm shall offend you,
      Passing the Main;
Nor Billow threat in vain,
    So Sacred a Train,
Till the Gods that defend you,
    Restore you again.

3

See at your blest returning
    Rage disappears;
The Widow'd Isle in Mourning
    Dries up her Tears,
  With Flowers the Meads adorning,
    Pleasure appears,
And love dispels the Nations causeless fears.

                [*Albion and Albanius*, 1685, ACT II]

XLIX

1

From the low Palace of old Father Ocean,
come we in pity your cares to deplore:
Sea-raceing Dolphins are train'd for our Motion,
Moony Tides swelling to rowl us a-shore.

2

Ev'ry Nymph of the Flood, her Tresses rending,
Throws off her Armlet of Pearl in the Main;
Neptune in anguish his Charge unattending,
Vessels are foundring, and Vows are in vain.

[*Albion and Albanius*, 1685, ACT III]

L

1

Albion, lov'd of Gods and Men,
Prince of Peace too mildly Reigning,
Cease thy sorrow and complaining;
Thou shalt be restor'd agen:
Albion, lov'd of Gods and Men.

2

Still thou art the care of Heav'n,
In thy Youth to Exile driv'n:
Heav'n thy ruin then prevented,
Till the guilty Land repented:

In thy Age, when none could aid Thee,
Foes conspir'd, and Friends betray'd Thee;
To the brink of danger driv'n,
Still thou art the Care of Heav'n.

[*Albion and Albanius*, 1685, ACT III]

LI

1

Albion, Hail; The Gods present Thee,
All the richest of their Treasures,
Peace and Pleasures,
To content Thee,
Dancing their eternal measures.

2

But above all humane blessing;
Take a Warlike Loyal Brother,
Never Prince had such another:
Conduct, Courage, truth expressing,
All Heroick worth possessing.
Chor. of all.　But above all, *&c.*

[*Albion and Albanius*, 1685, ACT III]

LII

A New
SONG.

1

Sylvia the fair, in the bloom of Fifteen,
Felt an innocent warmth, as she lay on the green;
She had heard of a pleasure, and something she guest
By the towzing & tumbling & touching her Breast;
She saw the men eager, but was at a loss,
What they meant by their sighing, & kissing so close;
  By their praying and whining
  And clasping and twining,
  And panting and wishing,
  And sighing and kissing
  And sighing and kissing so close.

2

Ah she cry'd, ah for a languishing Maid
In a Country of Christians to die without aid!
Not a Whig, or a Tory, or Trimmer at least,
Or a Protestant Parson, or Catholick Priest,
To instruct a young Virgin, that is at a loss
What they meant by their sighing, & kissing so close!
  By their praying and whining
  And clasping and twining,
  And panting and wishing,
  And sighing and kissing
  And sighing and kissing so close.

3

Cupid in Shape of a Swayn did appear,
He saw the sad wound, and in pity drew near,
Then show'd her his Arrow, and bid her not fear,
For the pain was no more than a Maiden may bear;
When the balm was infus'd she was not at a loss,
What they meant by their sighing & kissing so close;
 By their praying and whining,
 And clasping and twining,
 And panting and wishing,
 And sighing and kissing,
 And sighing and kissing so close.

[Sylvae, 1685]

LIII

SONG.

I

Go tell *Amynta* gentle Swain,
I wou'd not die nor dare complain,
Thy tuneful Voice with numbers joyn,
Thy words will more prevail than mine;
To Souls oppress'd and dumb with grief,
The Gods ordain this kind releif;
That Musick shou'd in sounds convey,
What dying Lovers dare not say.

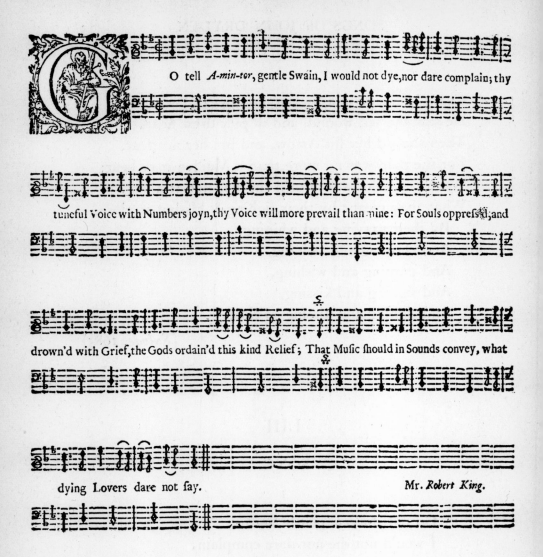

O tell *A-min-tor*, gentle Swain, I would not dye, nor dare complain; thy

tuneful Voice with Numbers joyn, thy Voice will more prevail than mine: For Souls oppreſs'd, and

drown'd with Grief, the Gods ordain'd this kind Relief; That Muſic ſhould in Sounds convey, what

dying Lovers dare not ſay.   Mr. *Robert King.*

II.

A Sigh, or Tear, perhaps ſhe'd give,
But Love on Pity cannot live;
Tell her, That Hearts for Hearts were made,
And Love with Love is only paid:
Tell her, My Pains ſo faſt encreaſe,
That ſoon they will be paſt Redreſs;
For ah! the Wretch that ſpeechleſs lies,
Attends but Death to cloſe his Eyes.

Song LIII. [*The Theater of Music*, 1685, I, 30]

2

A Sigh or Tear perhaps she'll give,
But love on pitty cannot live.
Tell her that Hearts for Hearts were made,
And love with love is only paid.
Tell her my pains so fast encrease,
That soon they will be past redress;
But ah! the Wretch that speechless lyes,
Attends but Death to close his Eyes.

[*Sylvae*, 1685]

LIV

1686 — Converted to Catholicism

A Song for St CECILIA's Day, 1687.

WRITTEN *set 1739*

By *John Dryden*, Esq; and Compos'd by Mr. *John*
(1631-1700) *Baptist Draghi*.

heroic couplet

I

From Harmony, from heav'nly Harmony
  This universal Frame began.
When Nature underneath a heap
  Of jarring Atomes lay,
  And cou'd not heave her Head,
The tuneful Voice was heard from high,
  Arise ye more than dead.
Then cold, and hot, and moist, and dry,

In order to their stations leap,
   And Musick's pow'r obey.
From Harmony, from heav'nly Harmony
   This universal Frame began:
   From Harmony to Harmony
Through all the compass of the Notes it ran,
The Diapason closing full in Man.

2

What Passion cannot Musick raise and quell!
   When *Jubal* struck the corded Shell,
   His list'ning Brethren stood around
   And wond'ring, on their Faces fell
   To worship that Celestial Sound.
Less than a God they thought there cou'd not dwell
   Within the hollow of that Shell
   That spoke so sweetly and so well.
What Passion cannot Musick raise and quell!

3

The Trumpets loud Clangor
   Excites us to Arms
With shrill Notes of Anger
   And mortal Alarms.
The double double double beat
   Of the thundring Drum
Cryes, heark the Foes come;
Charge, Charge, 'tis too late to retreat.

4

The soft complaining FLUTE
In dying Notes discovers
The Woes of hopeless Lovers,
Whose Dirge is whisper'd by the warbling LUTE.

5

Sharp VIOLINS proclaim
Their jealous Pangs, and Desperation,
Fury, frantick Indignation,
Depth of Pains, and height of Passion,
    For the fair, disdainful Dame.

6

But oh! what Art can teach
    What human Voice can reach
The sacred ORGANS praise?
Notes inspiring holy Love,
Notes that wing their heav'nly ways
    To mend the Choires above.

7

Orpheus cou'd lead the savage race;
And Trees unrooted left their place;
    Sequacious of the Lyre:
But bright *CECILIA* rais'd the wonder high'r;
When to her ORGAN, vocal Breath was giv'n
An Angel heard, and straight appear'd
    Mistaking Earth for Heaven.

Grand CHORUS

As from the pow'r of sacred Lays
  The Spheres began to move,
And sung the great Creator's praise
  To all the bless'd above;
So when the last and dreadful hour
This crumbling Pageant shall devour,
The TRUMPET *shall be heard on high,*
The Dead shall live, the Living die,
And MUSICK *shall untune the Sky.*

[Broadside edition, 1687]

LV

1

What shall I do to show how much I love her?
  How many Millions of Sigh's can suffice?
That which wins other Hearts, never can move her,
  Those common methods of Love she'll despise.

2

I will love more than Man e're lov'd before me,
  Gaze on her all the Day, melt all the Night;
Till for her own sake at last she'll implore me,
  To love her less to preserve our delight.

3

Since Gods themselves could not ever be loving,
  Men must have breathing Recruits for new Joys;

I wish my Love could be always improving,
  Tho eager Love more than Sorrow destroys.

4

In Fair *Aurelia*'s Arms leave me expiring,
  To be Embalm'd by the Sweets of her Breath,
To the last Moment I'll still be desiring:
  Never had *Hero* so glorious a Death.

[*The Prophetess*, 1690, ACT III]

LVI

SONG.

1

Celia, that I once was blest
Is now the Torment of my Brest;
Since to curse me, you bereave me
Of the Pleasures I possest:
Cruel Creature, to deceive me!
First to love, and then to leave me!

2

Had you the Bliss refus'd to grant,
Then I had never known the want:
But possessing once the Blessing,
Is the Cause of my Complaint:
Once possessing is but tasting;
'Tis no Bliss that is not lasting.

3

Celia now is mine no more;
But I am hers; and must adore:
Nor to leave her will endeavour;
Charms, that captiv'd me before,
No unkindness can dissever;
Love that's true, is Love for ever.

[*Amphitryon*, 1690, ACT III]

LVII

Mercury's SONG to *Phædra*.

1

Fair *Iris* I love, and hourly I dye,
But not for a Lip, nor a languishing Eye:
She's fickle and false, and there we agree;
For I am as false, and as fickle as she:
We neither believe what either can say;
And, neither believing, we neither betray.

2

'Tis civil to swear, and say things of course;
We mean not the taking for better for worse.
When present, we love; when absent, agree:
I think not of *Iris*, nor *Iris* of me:
The Legend of Love no Couple can find
So easie to part, or so equally join'd.

[*Amphitryon*, 1690, ACT IV]

LVIII

A Pastoral Dialogue betwixt Thyrsis *and* Iris.

I

Thyrsis. Fair *Iris* and her Swain
    Were in a shady Bow'r;
Where *Thyrsis* long in vain
    Had sought the Shepherd's hour:
At length his Hand advancing upon her snowy
    Breast;
    He said, O kiss me longer,
    And longer yet and longer,
      If you will make me Blest.

2

Iris. An easie yielding Maid,
    By trusting is undone;
Our Sex is oft betray'd,
    By granting Love too soon.
If you desire to gain me, your Suff'rings to re-
    dress;
    Prepare to love me longer,
    And longer yet, and longer,
      Before you shall possess.

3

Thyrsis. The little Care you show,
    Of all my Sorrows past;
Makes Death appear too slow,

And Life too long to last.
Fair *Iris* kiss me kindly, in pity of my Fate;
And kindly still, and kindly,
Before it be too late.

4

Iris.   You fondly Court your Bliss,
And no Advances make;
'Tis not for Maids to kiss,
But 'tis for Men to take.
So you may Kiss me kindly, and I will not
rebell;
And kindly still, and kindly,
But Kiss me not and tell.

A RONDEAU.

Chorus.   Thus at the height we love and live,
And fear not to be poor:
We give, and give, and give, and give,
Till we can give no more:
But what to day will take away,
To morrow will restore.
Thus at the heighth we love and live,
And fear not to be poor.

[*Amphitryon*, 1690, ACT IV]

LIX

Woden, first to thee,
A Milk white Steed, in Battle won,
We have Sacrific'd.
Chor.   We have Sacrific'd.
Vers.   Let our next Oblation be,
To *Thor*, thy thundring Son,
Of such another.
Chor.   We have Sacrific'd.
Vers.   A third; (of *Friezeland* breed was he,)
To *Woden*'s Wife, and to *Thor*'s Mother:
And now we have atton'd all three
We have Sacrific'd.
Chor.   We have Sacrific'd.
2 Voc.   The White Horse Neigh'd aloud.
To *Woden* thanks we render.
To *Woden*, we have vow'd.
Chor.   To *Woden*, our Defender.
Vers.   The Lot is Cast, and *Tanfan* pleas'd:
Chor.   Of Mortal Cares you shall be eas'd,
Brave Souls to be renown'd in Story.
Honour prizing,
Death despising,
Fame acquiring
By Expiring,
Dye, and reap the fruit of Glory.
Brave Souls to be renown'd in Story.
Vers.   I call ye all,

To *Woden*'s Hall;
Your Temples round
With Ivy bound,
In Goblets Crown'd,
And plenteous Bowls of burnish'd Gold;
Where you shall Laugh,
And dance and quaff,
The Juice, that makes the Britons bold.

[*King Arthur*, 1691, ACT I]

LX

I

Come if you dare, our Trumpets sound;
Come if you dare, the Foes rebound:
We come, we come, we come, we come,
Says the double, double, double Beat of the Thundring
        Drum.

2

Now they charge on amain,
Now they rally again:
The Gods from above the Mad Labour behold,
And pity Mankind that will perish for Gold.

3

The Fainting *Saxons* quit their Ground,
Their Trumpets Languish in the Sound;
They fly, they fly, they fly, they fly;
Victoria, *Victoria*, the Bold *Britons* cry.

4

Now the Victory's won,
To the Plunder we run:
We return to our Lasses like Fortunate Traders,
Triumphant with Spoils of the Vanquish'd Invaders.

[*King Arthur*, 1691, ACT I]

LXI

Phil.⎱ Hither this way, this way bend,
sings.⎰ Trust not that Malicious Fiend:
        Those are false deluding Lights,
        Wafted far and near by Sprights.
        Trust 'em not, for they'll deceive ye;
        And in Bogs and Marshes leave ye.
Chor. of Phil. Spirits.   Hither this way, this way bend.
Chor. of Grimb. Spirits.   This way, this way bend.
Phil.⎱ If you step, no Danger thinking,
sings.⎰ Down you fall, a Furlong sinking:
        'Tis a Fiend who has annoy'd ye;
        Name but Heav'n, and he'll avoid ye.
Chor. of Phil. Spirits.   Hither this way, this way bend.
Chor. of Grimb. Spirits.   This way, this way bend.
Philidels Spirits.   Trust not that Malicious Fiend.
Grimbalds Spirits.   Trust me, I am no Malicious Fiend.
Philidels Spirits.   Hither this way, &c.
Philidel sings.   Hither this way.

Chor. of Phil. Spirits. Hither this way, this way bend.
Chor. of Grimb. Spirits. This way, this way bend.
Philidels Spirits. Trust not that Malicious Fiend.
Grimb. Spirits. Trust me, I am no Malicious Fiend.
Philidels Spirits. Hither this way, *&c.*
Phil. singing. Come follow, follow, follow me.
Chor.   Come follow, *&c.*
            And me.   And me.   And me.   And me.
Vers. 2 Voc. And Green-Sward all your way shall be.
Chor.   Come follow, *&c.*
Vers.   No *Goblin* or *Elf* shall dare to offend ye.
Chor.   No, no, no, *&c.*
            No *Goblin* or *Elf* shall dare to offend ye.
Vers. 3 Voc. We Brethren of Air,
            You *Hero*'s will bear,
            To the Kind and the Fair that attend ye.
Chor.   We Brethren, *&c.*

[*King Arthur*, 1691, ACT II]

LXII

I

Let not a Moon-born Elf mislead ye,
From your Prey, and from your Glory.
Too far, Alas, he has betray'd ye:
Follow the Flames, that wave before ye:
Sometimes sev'n, and sometimes one;
Hurry, hurry, hurry, hurry on.

2

See, see, the Footsteps plain appearing,
That way *Oswald* chose for flying:
Firm is the Turff, and fit for bearing,
Where yonder Pearly Dews are lying.
Far he cannot hence be gone;
Hurry, hurry, hurry, hurry on.

[*King Arthur*, 1691, ACT II]

LXIII

1

How blest are Shepherds, how happy their Lasses,
While Drums & Trumpets are sounding Alarms!
Over our Lowly Sheds all the Storm passes;
And when we die, 'tis in each others Arms.
All the Day on our Herds, and Flocks employing;
All the Night on our Flutes, and in enjoying.
Chor. All the Day, &c.

2

Bright Nymphs of *Britain*, with Graces attended,
Let not your Days without Pleasure expire;
Honour's but empty, and when Youth is ended,
All Men will praise you, but none will desire.
Let not Youth fly away without Contenting;
Age will come time enough, for your Repenting.
Chor. Let not Youth, &c.

[*King Arthur*, 1691, ACT II]

LXIV

1

Shepherd, Shepherd, leave Decoying,
  Pipes are sweet, a Summers Day;
But a little after Toying,
  Women have the Shot to Pay.

2

Here are Marriage-Vows for signing,
  Set their Marks that cannot write:
After that, without Repining,
  Play and Welcom, Day and Night.

3

Chor.⎫ Come, Shepherds, lead up, a lively Measure;
of all.⎭ The Cares of Wedlock, are Cares of Pleasure:
But whether Marriage bring Joy, or Sorrow,
Make sure of this Day, and hang to Morrow.

[*King Arthur*, 1691, ACT II]

LXV

We must work, we must haste;
Noon-Tyde Hour, is almost past:
Sprights, that glimmer in the Sun,
Into Shades already run.
Osmond will be here, anon.

[*King Arthur*, 1691, ACT III]

LXVI

Thus, thus I infuse
These Soveraign Dews.
Fly back, ye Films, that Cloud her sight,
And you, ye Chrystal Humours bright,
Your Noxious Vapours purg'd away,
Recover, and admit the Day.
Now cast your Eyes abroad, and see
All but me.

[*King Arthur*, 1691, ACT III]

LXVII

1

Man sings.   Oh Sight, the Mother of Desires,
What Charming Objects dost thou yield!
'Tis sweet, when tedious Night expires,
To see the Rosie Morning guild
The Mountain-Tops, and paint the
Field!
But, when *Clorinda* comes in sight,
She makes the Summers Day more bright;
And when she goes away, 'tis Night.

Chor.   When Fair *Clorinda* comes in sight, *&c.*

2

Wom. sings.   'Tis sweet the Blushing Morn to view;
And Plains adorn'd with Pearly Dew:

But such cheap Delights to see,
  Heaven and Nature,
  Give each Creature;
They have Eyes, as well as we.
  This is the Joy, all Joys above,
    To see, to see,
    That only she,
    That only she we love!

Chor.   This is the Joy, all Joys above, &c.

3

Man sings.   And, if we may discover,
What Charms both Nymph and Lover,
  'Tis, when the Fair at Mercy lies,
With Kind and Amorous Anguish,
To Sigh, to Look, to Languish,
  On each others Eyes!

Chor. of all ⎫
Men & Wom. ⎭   And if we may discover, &c.

[*King Arthur*, 1691, ACT III]

LXVIII

I

Cup. sings. What ho, thou *Genius* of the Clime, what ho!
Ly'st thou asleep beneath those Hills of Snow?
Stretch out thy Lazy Limbs; Awake, awake,
And Winter from thy Furry Mantle shake.

2

Genius. What Power art thou, who from below,
Hast made me Rise, unwillingly, and slow,
From Beds of Everlasting Snow!
See'st thou not how stiff, and wondrous old,
Far unfit to bear the bitter Cold,
I can scarcely move, or draw my Breath;
Let me, let me, Freeze again to Death.

3

Cupid. Thou Doting Fool, forbear, forbear;
What, Dost thou Dream of Freezing here?
At Loves appearing, all the Skie clearing,
The Stormy Winds their Fury spare:
Winter subduing, and Spring renewing,
My Beams create a more Glorious Year.
Thou Doting Fool, forbear, forbear;
What, Dost thou Dream of Freezing here?

4

Genius. Great Love, I know thee now;
Eldest of the Gods art Thou:
Heav'n and Earth, by Thee were made.
Humane Nature,
Is Thy Creature,
Every where Thou art obey'd.

5

Cupid.   No part of my Dominion shall be waste,
                To spread my Sway, and sing my Praise,
                Ev'n here I will a People raise,
                Of kind embracing Lovers, and embrac'd.

[*King Arthur*, 1691, ACT III]

LXIX

1

Man.   See, see, we assemble,
                Thy Revels to hold:
                Though quiv'ring with Cold,
            We Chatter and Tremble.

2

Cupid.   'Tis I, 'tis I, 'tis I, that have warm'd ye;
                In spight of Cold Weather,
                I've brought ye together:
            'Tis I, 'tis I, 'tis I, that have arm'd ye.

3

Chor.   'Tis Love, 'tis Love, 'tis Love that has warm'd us;
                In spight of Cold Weather,
                He brought us together:
            'Tis Love, 'tis Love, 'tis Love that has arm'd us.

[*King Arthur*, 1691, ACT III]

LXX

I

Sound a Parley, ye Fair, and surrender;
Set your selves, and your Lovers at ease;
   He's a Grateful Offender
   Who Pleasure dare seize:
But the Whining Pretender
   Is sure to displease.

2

Since the Fruit of Desire is possessing,
   'Tis Unmanly to Sigh and Complain;
When we Kneel for Redressing,
   We move your Disdain:
Love was made for a Blessing,
   And not for a Pain.

[*King Arthur*, 1691, ACT III]

LXXI

I

1 Syren.   O pass not on, but stay,
   And waste the Joyous Day
   With us in gentle Play:
Unbend to Love, unbend thee:
   O lay thy Sword aside,
   And other Arms provide;

For other Wars attend thee,
And sweeter to be try'd.

Chor.   For other Wars, &c.

2

Both sing. Two Daughters of this Aged Stream are we;
And both our Sea-green Locks have comb'd
for thee;
Come Bathe with us an Hour or two,
Come Naked in, for we are so;
What Danger from a Naked Foe?
Come Bathe with us, come Bathe, and share,
What Pleasures in the Floods appear;
We'll beat the Waters till they bound,
And Circle, round, around, around,
And Circle round, around.

[*King Arthur*, 1691, ACT IV]

LXXII

Song.

I

How happy the Lover,
How easie his Chain,
How pleasing his Pain?
How sweet to discover!
He sighs not in vain.
For Love every Creature

Is form'd by his Nature;
No Joys are above
The Pleasures of Love.

2

In vain are our Graces,
   In vain are your Eyes,
   If Love you despise;
When Age furrows Faces,
   'Tis time to be wise.
Then use the short Blessing,
That Flies in Possessing:
No Joys are above
The Pleasures of Love.

[*King Arthur*, 1691, ACT IV]

LXXIII

Ye Blust'ring Brethren of the Skies,
Whose Breath has ruffl'd all the Watry Plain,
   Retire, and let *Britannia* Rise,
In Triumph o'er the Main.
   Serene and Calm, and void of fear,
   The Queen of Islands must appear:
   Serene and Calm, as when the Spring
   The New-Created World began,
   And Birds on Boughs did softly sing,
   Their Peaceful Homage paid to Man,
   While *Eurus* did his Blasts forbear,

In favour of the Tender Year.
Retreat, Rude Winds, Retreat,
To Hollow Rocks, your Stormy Seat;
There swell your Lungs, and vainly, vainly threat.

[*King Arthur*, 1691, ACT V]

LXXIV

Round thy Coasts, Fair Nymph of *Britain*,
    For thy Guard our Waters flow:
Proteus all his Herd admitting,
    On thy Greens to Graze below.
Foreign Lands thy Fishes Tasting,
Learn from thee Luxurious Fasting.

[*King Arthur*, 1691, ACT V]

LXXV

Song of three Parts.

I

For Folded Flocks, on Fruitful Plains,
The Shepherds and the Farmers Gains,
    Fair *Britain* all the World outvyes;
And *Pan*, as in *Arcadia* Reigns,
    Where Pleasure mixt with Profit lyes.

2

Though *Jasons* Office was Fam'd of old,
The *British* Wool is growing Gold;
　　No Mines can more of Wealth supply:
It keeps the Peasant from the Cold,
　　And takes for Kings the *Tyrian* Dye.

　　　　　　　　　[*King Arthur*, 1691, ACT v]

LXXVI

I

Com.　　Your Hay it is Mow'd, & your Corn is Reap'd;
　　　　Your Barns will be full, and your Hovels heap'd:
　　　　　Come, my Boys, come;
　　　　　Come, my Boys, come;
　　　　And merrily Roar out Harvest Home;
　　　　　Harvest Home,
　　　　　Harvest Home;
　　　　And merrily Roar out Harvest Home.
Chorus.　Come, my Boys, come, *&c.*

2

1 Man.　We ha' cheated the Parson, we'll cheat him agen;
　　　　For why shou'd a Blockhead ha' One in Ten?
　　　　　One in Ten,
　　　　　One in Ten,
　　　　For why shou'd a Blockhead ha' One in Ten?
Chorus.　　One in Ten,
　　　　　One in Ten;
　　　　For why shou'd a Blockhead ha' One in Ten?

3

2.   For Prating so long like a Book-learn'd Sot,
        Till Pudding and Dumplin burn to Pot;
           Burn to Pot,
           Burn to Pot;
        Till Pudding and Dumplin burn to Pot.

Chorus.   Burn to pot, *&c.*

4

3.   We'll toss off our Ale till we canno' stand,
        And Hoigh for the Honour of Old *England:*
           Old *England,*
           Old *England;*
        And Hoigh for the Honour of Old *England.*

Chorus.   Old *England, &c.*

                [*King Arthur,* 1691, ACT V]

LXXVII

I

Fairest Isle, all Isles Excelling,
    Seat of Pleasures, and of Loves;
Venus here, will chuse her Dwelling,
    And forsake her *Cyprian* Groves.

2

Cupid, from his Fav'rite Nation,
    Care and Envy will Remove;
Jealousie, that poysons Passion,
    And Despair that dies for Love.

3

Gentle Murmurs, sweet Complaining,
  Sighs that blow the Fire of Love;
Soft Repulses, kind Disdaining,
  Shall be all the Pains you prove.

4

Every Swain shall pay his Duty,
  Grateful every Nymph shall prove;
And as these Excel in Beauty,
  Those shall be Renown'd for Love.

[*King Arthur*, 1691, ACT V]

LXXVIII

1

St. *George*, the Patron of our Isle,
  A Soldier, and a Saint,
On that Auspicious Order smile,
  Which Love and Arms will plant.

2

Our Natives not alone appear
  To Court this Martiall Prize;
But Foreign Kings, Adopted here,
  Their Crowns at Home despise.

3

Our Soveraign High, in Aweful State,
His Honours shall bestow;
And see his Sceptr'd Subjects wait
On his Commands below.

[*King Arthur*, 1691, ACT V]

LXXIX

SONG.

1

No no, poor suff'ring Heart no Change endeavour,
Choose to sustain the smart, rather than leave her;
My ravish'd Eyes behold such Charms about her,
I can dye with her, but not live without her.
One tender Sigh of hers to see me Languish,
Will more than pay the price of my past Anguish:
Beware O cruel Fair, how you smile on me,
'Twas a kind Look of yours that has undone me.

2

Love has in store for me one happy Minute,
And She will end my pain who did begin it;
Then no day void of Bliss, or Pleasure leaving,
Ages shall slide away without perceiving:
Cupid shall guard the Door the more to please us,
And keep out Time and Death when they would seize us:
Time and Death shall depart, and say in flying,
Love has found out a way to Live by Dying.

[*Cleomenes*, 1692, ACT II]

LXXX

SONG
TO A
Fair, Young LADY,
Going out of the TOWN
In the
SPRING.
By Mr. *DRYDEN*.

I

Ask not the Cause, why sullen *Spring*
 So long delays her Flow'rs to bear;
Why warbling Birds forget to sing,
 And Winter Storms invert the Year?
Chloris is gone; and Fate provides
To make it *Spring*, where she resides.

2

Chloris is gone, the Cruel Fair;
 She cast not back a pitying Eye:
But left her Lover in Despair;
 To sigh, to languish, and to die:
Ah, how can those fair Eyes endure
To give the Wounds they will not cure!

3

Great God of Love, why hast thou made
 A Face that can all Hearts command,
That all Religions can invade,

And change the Laws of ev'ry Land?
Where thou hadst plac'd such Pow'r before,
Thou shou'dst have made her Mercy more.

4

When *Chloris* to the Temple comes,
    Adoring Crowds before her fall;
She can restore the Dead from Tombs,
    And ev'ry Life but mine recall.
I only am by Love design'd
To be the Victim for Mankind.

[*Examen Poeticum*, 1693]

LXXXI

Veni Creator Spiritus,
Translated in
PARAPHRASE.
BY
Mr. *DRYDEN*.

I

Creator Spirit, by whose aid
The World's Foundations first were laid,
Come visit ev'ry pious Mind;
Come pour thy Joys on Human Kind:
From Sin, and Sorrow set us free;
And make thy Temples worthy Thee.

ASK not the cause, why sul-len Spring, so long de-lays her Flowrs to bear, why warbling Birds, why

warb—ling, warb————ling Birds forget to Sing, and Winter Storms in--vest the year

Clo-ris is gone, Clo—ris is gone, and Fate, and Fate provides to make it Spring, where

she re--sides to make it Spring, where she re--sides: Clo-ris is gone, the cru—el Fair, she

cast not back a pi--ty-ing Eye; but left her Lover, but left her Lo———————ver

in despair, to Sigh, to Languish and to die, ah! how can those fair Eyes endure to

give, to give the wounds, they will not cure, to give the wounds they will not cure.

2

O, Source of uncreated Light,
The Father's promis'd *Paraclite!*
Thrice Holy Fount, thrice Holy Fire,
Our Hearts with Heav'nly Love inspire;
Come, and thy Sacred Unction bring
To Sanctifie us, while we sing!

3

Plenteous of Grace, descend from high,
Rich in thy sev'n-fold Energy!
Thou strength of his Almighty Hand,
Whose Pow'r does Heav'n and Earth command:
Proceeding Spirit, our Defence, ⎫
Who do'st the Gift of Tongues dispence, ⎬
And crown'st thy Gift, with Eloquence! ⎭

4

Refine and purge our Earthy Parts;
But, oh, inflame and fire our Hearts!
Our Frailties help, our Vice controul;
Submit the Senses to the Soul;
And when Rebellious they are grown,
Then, lay thy hand, and hold 'em down.

5

Chace from our Minds th' Infernal Foe;
And Peace, the fruit of Love, bestow:
And, lest our Feet shou'd step astray,
Protect, and guide us in the way.

6

Make us Eternal Truths receive,
And practise, all that we believe:
Give us thy self, that we may see
The Father and the Son, by thee.

7

Immortal Honour, endless Fame
Attend th' Almighty Father's Name:
The Saviour Son, be glorify'd,
Who for lost Man's Redemption dy'd:
And equal Adoration be
Eternal *Paraclete*, to thee.

[*Examen Poeticum*, 1693]

LXXXII

RONDELAY.
BY
Mr. *DRYDEN*.

I

Chloe found *Amyntas* lying
    All in Tears, upon the Plain;
Sighing to himself, and crying,
    Wretched I, to love in vain!
Kiss me, Dear, before my dying;
    Kiss me once, and ease my pain!

A Song set by Mr. *John Gilbert.*

Hlo -e found A—myntas ly--ing, all in Tears up—on the Plain; sighing
to him—self and crying, wretched I, to love in vain! Kiſs me, Kiſs me,
Dear, be—fore my dying; Kiſs me once and eaſe my pain. *Roundeau.*

II.
Sighing to himſelf and crying,
Wretched I, to Love in vain:
Ever ſcorning and denying,
To reward your faithfull Swain;
Kiſs me, Dear, before my dying,
Kiſs me once and eaſe my pain.

III.
Ever ſcorning and denying,
To reward your faithfull Swain:
Chloe, laughing at his crying,
Told him that he lov'd in vain;
Kiſs me, Dear, before my dying,
Kiſs me once and eaſe my pain.

IV.
Chloe laughing at his crying,
Told him that he lov'd in vain;
But repenting and complying,
When He Kis'd, She Kis'd again,
Kis'd Him up before His dying,
Kis'd Him up and eas'd His pain.

SONG LXXXII. [*Deliciae Musicae*, 1695, II, 2]

2

Sighing to himself, and crying
  Wretched I, to love in vain:
Ever scorning and denying
  To reward your faithful Swain:
Kiss me, Dear, before my dying;
  Kiss me once, and ease my pain!

3

Ever scorning, and denying
  To reward your faithful Swain;
Chloe, laughing at his crying,
  Told him that he lov'd in vain:
Kiss me, Dear, before my dying;
  Kiss me once, and ease my pain!

4

Chloe, laughing at his crying,
  Told him that he lov'd in vain:
But repenting, and complying,
  When he kiss'd, she kiss'd again:
Kiss'd him up, before his dying;
  Kiss'd him up, and eas'd his pain.

[*Examen Poeticum*, 1693]

LXXXIII

Song of Jealousie.

I

What State of Life can be so blest
As Love, that warms a Lover's Breast?
Two Souls in one, the same desire
To grant the Bliss, and to require!
But if in Heav'n a Hell we find,
'Tis all from thee,
O Jealousie!
'Tis all from thee,
O Jealousie!
Thou Tyrant, Tyrant Jealousie,
Thou Tyrant of the Mind!

2

All other ills, tho sharp they prove,
Serve to refine, and perfect Love:
In absence, or unkind disdain,
Sweet Hope relieves the Lover's pain:
But ah, no Cure but Death we find,
To set us free
From Jealousie:
O Jealousie!
Thou Tyrant, Tyrant Jealousie,
Thou Tyrant of the Mind.

A Song in the laſt new Play call'd *Love Triumphant*, &c.
Set by Mr. *John Eccles*, and Sung by Mrs. *Hudſon*.

WHat ſtate of life can be ſo bleſt, as love that warms a lo—vers breaſt;

two ſouls in one the ſame de-ſire, to grant the bliſs and to require; but

if in Heav'n a Hell we find, 'tis all from thee, oh! Jealouſie, oh! oh! oh!

oh! oh! Jealou—ſie, thou tyrant, tyrant. Jealou—ſie thou ty————rant,

Jealouſie, oh! oh! oh! oh! oh! Jealouſie, oh! oh! oh! Jealouſie thou

ty—rant of the mind.

II.

All other Ills tho' ſharp they prove,
Serve to refine and perfect love;
In abſence or unkind diſdain,
Sweet hope relieve the lover's pain:
But oh! no cure but death we find,
To ſet us free from Jealouſie.　　　　　*Oh! oh! &c.*

II.

Falſe in thy glaſs all Objects are,
Some ſet too near, and ſome too farr,
Thou art the fire of endleſs night,
The fire that burns, and gives no Light;
All Torments of the damn'd we find,
In only thee, oh! Jealouſie.

SONG LXXXIII. [*Thesaurus Musicus*, 1694, II, 31]

3

False, in thy Glass all Objects are,
Some set too near, and some too far:
Thou art the Fire of endless Night,
The Fire that burns, and gives no Light
All Torments of the Damn'd we find
In only thee
O Jealousie!
Thou Tyrant, Tyrant Jealousie,
Thou Tyrant of the Mind!

[*Love Triumphant*, 1694, ACT III]

LXXXIV

Song for a GIRL.

1

Young I am, and yet unskill'd
How to make a Lover yield:
How to keep, or how to gain,
When to Love; and when to feign:

2

Take me, take me, some of you,
While I yet am Young and True;
E're I can my Soul disguise;
Heave my Breasts, and roul my Eyes.

A Song set by Mr. *John Eccles.* In Love *Tryumphant* by Mr. *Dryden.*

YOUNG I am and yet un—skill'd, how to make a

Lo — ver yeild; how to keep, or how to gain,

when to love, and when to feign: Take me, take me some of

you, while I yet am young and true; e're I can my

Soul disguise, heave my Breasts, heave my Breasts and

rowl my Eyes.

SONG LXXXIV. [*The Gentleman's Journal,* January and February, 1694, p. 35]

3

Stay not till I learn the way,
How to Lye, and to Betray:
He that has me first, is blest,
For I may deceive the rest.

4

Cou'd I find a blooming Youth;
Full of Love, and full of Truth,
Brisk, and of a janty meen,
I shou'd long to be Fifteen.

[*Love Triumphant*, 1694, ACT V]

LXXXV

AN

ODE,

ON THE

DEATH

OF

Mr. Henry Purcell.

The ODE.

I

Mark how the Lark and Linnet Sing,
With rival Notes
They strain their warbling Throats,
To welcome in the Spring.

But in the close of Night,
When *Philomel* begins her Heav'nly lay,
They cease their mutual spight,
Drink in her Musick with delight,
And list'ning and silent, and silent and list'ning,
and list'ning and silent obey.

2

So ceas'd the rival Crew when *Purcell* came,
They Sung no more, or only Sung his Fame.
Struck dumb they all admir'd the God-like Man,
The God-like Man,
Alas, too soon retir'd,
As He too late began.
We beg not Hell, our *Orpheus* to restore,
Had He been there,
Their Sovereigns fear
Had sent Him back before.
The pow'r of Harmony too well they know,
He long e'er this had Tun'd their jarring Sphere,
And left no Hell below.

3

The Heav'nly Quire, who heard his Notes from high,
Let down the Scale of Musick from the Sky:
They handed him along,
And all the way He taught, and all the way they Sung.
Ye Brethren of the *Lyre*, and tunefull Voice,
Lament his lott: but at your own rejoyce.

Now live secure and linger out your days,
The Gods are pleas'd alone with *Purcell*'s *Layes*,
Nor know to mend their Choice.

[Folio edition, 1696]

LXXXVI

Alexander's Feast;
OR THE
POWER of MUSIQUE.
AN
ODE,
In Honour of
St. *CECILIA*'s Day.

I

'Twas at the Royal Feast, for *Persia* won,
     By *Philip*'s Warlike Son:
     Aloft in awful State
     The God-like Heroe sate
     On his Imperial Throne:
His valiant Peers were plac'd around;
Their Brows with Roses and with Myrtles bound.
     (So shou'd Desert in Arms be Crown'd:)
The Lovely *Thais* by his side,
Sate like a blooming *Eastern* Bride
In Flow'r of Youth and Beauty's Pride.
     Happy, happy, happy Pair!
     None but the Brave
     None but the Brave
     None but the Brave deserves the Fair.

CHORUS.

Happy, happy, happy Pair!
None but the Brave
None but the Brave
None but the Brave deserves the Fair.

2

Timotheus plac'd on high
  Amid the tuneful Quire,
  With flying Fingers touch'd the Lyre:
The trembling Notes ascend the Sky,
      And Heav'nly Joys inspire.
The Song began from *Jove*;
Who left his blissful Seats above,
(Such is the Pow'r of mighty Love.)
A Dragon's fiery Form bely'd the God:
Sublime on Radiant Spires He rode,
  When He to fair *Olympia* press'd:
  And while He sought her snowy Breast:
Then, round her slender Waste he curl'd,
And stamp'd an Image of himself, a Sov'raign of the World.
The list'ning Crowd admire the lofty Sound,
A present Deity, they shout around:
A present Deity the vaulted Roofs rebound.
      With ravish'd Ears
      The Monarch hears,
      Assumes the God,
      Affects to nod,
  And seems to shake the Spheres.

CHORUS.

With ravish'd Ears
The Monarch hears,
Assumes the God,
Affects to Nod,
And seems to shake the Spheres.

3

The Praise of *Bacchus* then, the sweet Musician sung;
Of *Bacchus* ever Fair, and ever Young:
The jolly God in Triumph comes;
Sound the Trumpets; beat the Drums;
Flush'd with a purple Grace
He shews his honest Face,
Now give the Hautboys breath; He comes, He comes.
Bacchus ever Fair and Young,
Drinking Joys did first ordain:
Bacchus Blessings are a Treasure;
Drinking is the Soldiers Pleasure;
Rich the Treasure,
Sweet the Pleasure;
Sweet is Pleasure after Pain.

CHORUS.

Bacchus Blessings are a Treasure,
Drinking is the Soldier's Pleasure;
Rich the Treasure,
Sweet the Pleasure;
Sweet is Pleasure after Pain.

4

Sooth'd with the Sound the King grew vain;
  Fought all his Battails o'er again;
And thrice He routed all his Foes; and thrice He slew the
    slain.
    The Master saw the Madness rise;
    His glowing Cheeks, his ardent Eyes;
    And while He Heav'n and Earth defy'd,
    Chang'd his hand, and check'd his Pride.
      He chose a Mournful Muse
      Soft Pity to infuse:
    He sung *Darius* Great and Good,
      By too severe a Fate,
    Fallen, fallen, fallen, fallen,
      Fallen from his high Estate
        And weltring in his Blood:
Deserted at his utmost Need,
By those his former Bounty fed:
On the bare Earth expos'd He lyes,
With not a Friend to close his Eyes.
    With down-cast Looks the joyless Victor sate,
    Revolveing in his alter'd Soul
      The various Turns of Chance below;
    And, now and then, a Sigh he stole;
      And Tears began to flow.

CHORUS.

  Revolveing in his alter'd Soul
    The various Turns of Chance below;
  And, now and then, a Sigh he stole;
    And Tears began to flow.

5

The Mighty Master smil'd to see
That Love was in the next Degree:
'Twas but a Kindred-Sound to move;
For Pity melts the Mind to Love.
  Softly sweet, in *Lydian* Measures,
  Soon He sooth'd his Soul to Pleasures.
  War, he sung, is Toil and Trouble;
  Honour but an empty Bubble.
    Never ending, still beginning,
  Fighting still, and still destroying,
    If the World be worth thy Winning,
  Think, O think, it worth Enjoying.
    Lovely *Thais* sits beside thee,
    Take the Good the Gods provide thee.
The Many rend the Skies, with loud Applause;
So Love was Crown'd, but Musique won the Cause.
  The Prince, unable to conceal his Pain,
     Gaz'd on the Fair
     Who caus'd his Care,
  And sigh'd and look'd, sigh'd and look'd,
  Sigh'd and look'd, and sigh'd again:
At length, with Love and Wine at once oppress'd,
The vanquish'd Victor sunk upon her Breast.

CHORUS.

  The Prince, unable to conceal his Pain,
    Gaz'd on the Fair
    Who caus'd his Care,

And sigh'd and look'd, sigh'd and look'd,
Sigh'd and look'd, and sigh'd again:
At length, with Love and Wine at once oppress'd,
The vanquish'd Victor sunk upon her Breast.

6

Now strike the Golden Lyre again:
A lowder yet, and yet a lowder Strain.
Break his Bands of Sleep asunder,
And rouze him, like a rattling Peal of Thunder.
  Hark, hark, the horrid Sound
   Has rais'd up his Head,
   As awak'd from the Dead,
  And amaz'd, he stares around.
Revenge, Revenge, *Timotheus* cries,
 See the Furies arise!
 See the Snakes that they rear,
 How they hiss in their Hair,
And the Sparkles that flash from their Eyes!
 Behold a ghastly Band,
 Each a Torch in his Hand!
Those are *Grecian* Ghosts, that in Battail were slayn,
  And unbury'd remain
  Inglorious on the Plain.
 Give the Vengeance due
 To the Valiant Crew.
Behold how they toss their Torches on high,
 How they point to the *Persian* Abodes,
And glitt'ring Temples of their Hostile Gods!

The Princes applaud, with a furious Joy;
And the King seyz'd a Flambeau, with Zeal to destroy;
    Thais led the Way,
    To light him to his Prey,
And, like another *Hellen*, fir'd another *Troy*.

CHORUS.

And the King seyz'd a Flambeau, with Zeal to destroy;
    Thais *led the Way,*
    To light him to his Prey,
And, like another Hellen, *fir'd another* Troy.

7

    Thus, long ago
  'Ere heaving Bellows learn'd to blow,
    While Organs yet were mute;
  Timotheus, to his breathing Flute,
    And sounding Lyre,
Cou'd swell the Soul to rage, or kindle soft Desire.
  At last Divine *Cecilia* came,
  Inventress of the Vocal Frame;
The sweet Enthusiast, from her Sacred Store,
    Enlarg'd the former narrow Bounds,
    And added Length to solemn Sounds,
With Nature's Mother-Wit, and Arts unknown before.
  Let old *Timotheus* yield the Prize,
    Or both divide the Crown;
  He rais'd a Mortal to the Skies;
    She drew an Angel down.

Grand CHORUS.

At last, Divine Cecilia *came,*
Inventress of the Vocal Frame;
The sweet Enthusiast, from her Sacred Store,
Enlarg'd the former narrow Bounds,
And added Length to solemn Sounds,
With Nature's Mother-Wit, and Arts unknown before.
Let old Timotheus *yield the Prize,*
Or both divide the Crown;
He rais'd a Mortal to the Skies;
She drew an Angel down.

[Folio edition, 1697]

LXXXVII

SONG of a *Scholar* and his *Mistress*, who being
Cross'd by their Friends, fell Mad for one
another; and now first meet in *Bedlam*.
Written by Mr. DRYDEN.

Phillis.   Look, look, I see — I see my Love appear:
             'Tis he — 'Tis he alone;
             For, like him, there is none:
             'Tis the dear, dear Man, 'tis thee, Dear.
Amyntas.   Hark! the Winds War;
             The foamy Waves roar;
             I see a Ship afar,

Tossing and Tossing, and making to the Shoar:
  But what's that I View,
  So Radiant of Hue,
St. *Hermo*, St. *Hermo*, that sits upon the Sails?
  Ah! No, no, no.
St. *Hermo*, Never, never shone so bright;
'Tis *Phillis*, only *Phillis*, can shoot so fair a
  Light:
'Tis *Phillis*, 'tis *Phillis*, that saves the Ship
  alone,
For all the Winds are hush'd, and the Storm
  is over-blown.

Phillis. Let me go, let me run, let me fly to his Arms.

Amyntas. If all the Fates combine,
  And all the Furies join,
  I'll force my way to *Phillis*, and break through
    the Charms.

Phillis. Shall I Marry the Man I love?
    And shall I conclude my Pains?
  Now blest be the Powers above,
  I feel the Blood bound in my Veins;
  With a lively Leap it began to move,
    And the Vapours leave my Brains.

Amyntas. Body join'd to Body, and Heart join'd to
    Heart,
    To make sure of the Cure;
  Go call the Man in Black, to mumble o're his
    part.

Phillis. But suppose he should stay —

Amyntas.   At worst if he delay;
   'Tis a Work must be done;
  We'll borrow but a Day,
   And the better the sooner begun.

CHORUS of Both.

At worst if he delay, &c.

[*The Pilgrim,* 1700]

LXXXVIII

THE
Secular Masque.
Written by Mr. *DRYDEN.*

Enter Janus.

Janus. *Chronos, Chronos,* mend thy Pace,
  An hundred times the rowling Sun
  Around the Radiant Belt has run
  In his revolving Race.
  Behold, behold, the Goal in sight,
  Spread thy Fans, and wing thy flight.
    Enter Chronos, *with a Scythe in his hand,*
    and a great Globe on his Back, which he
    sets down at his entrance.

Chronos. Weary, weary of my weight,
  Let me, let me drop my Freight,
   And leave the World behind.
  I could not bear

Another Year
The Load of Human-kind.
    Enter Momus *Laughing.*

Momus.   Ha! ha! ha! Ha! ha! ha! well hast thou done,
    To lay down thy Pack,
    And lighten thy Back,
The World was a Fool, e'er since it begun,
And since neither *Janus*, nor *Chronos*, nor I,
    Can hinder the Crimes,
    Or mend the Bad Times,
'Tis better to Laugh than to Cry.

Cho. of all 3.   *'Tis better to Laugh than to Cry.*

Janus.   Since *Momus* comes to laugh below,
    Old Time begin the Show,
That he may see, in every Scene,
What Changes in this Age have been,

Chronos.   Then Goddess of the Silver Bow begin.
    Horns, or Hunting-Musique within.
    Enter Diana.

Diana.   With Horns and with Hounds I waken the
    Day.
And hye to my Woodland walks away;
I tuck up my Robe, and am buskin'd soon,
And tye to my Forehead a wexing Moon.
I course the fleet Stagg, unkennel the Fox,
And chase the wild Goats or'e summets of
    Rocks,
With shouting and hooting we pierce thro'
    the Sky;

And Eccho turns Hunter, and doubles the
    Cry.

Cho. of all.   *With shouting and hooting, we pierce through*
    the Skie,

And Eccho turns Hunter, and doubles the Cry.

Janus.   Then our Age was in it's Prime,

Chronos.   Free from Rage.

Diana.   — — And free from Crime.

Momus.   A very Merry, Dancing, Drinking,

Laughing, Quaffing, and unthinking Time.

Cho. of all.   *Then our Age was in it's Prime,*

Free from Rage, and free from Crime,

A very Merry, Dancing, Drinking,

Laughing, Quaffing, and unthinking Time.

      Dance of Diana's *Attendants.*

      Enter Mars.

Mars.   Inspire the Vocal Brass, Inspire;

The World is past its Infant Age:

    Arms and Honour,

    Arms and Honour,

Set the Martial Mind on Fire,

And kindle Manly Rage.

Mars has lookt the Sky to Red;

And Peace, the Lazy Good, is fled.

Plenty, Peace, and Pleasure fly;

    The Sprightly Green

In *Woodland*-Walks, no more is seen;

The Sprightly Green, has drunk the *Tyrian*
    Dye.

Cho. of all.   *Plenty, Peace,* &c.

Mars.	Sound the Trumpet, Beat the Drum,
	Through all the World around;
	Sound a Reveille, Sound, Sound,
	The Warrior God is come.
Cho. of all.	*Sound the Trumpet,* &c.
Momus.	Thy Sword within the Scabbard keep,
	And let Mankind agree;
	Better the World were fast asleep,
	Than kept awake by Thee.
	The Fools are only thinner,
	With all our Cost and Care;
	But neither side a winner,
	For Things are as they were.
Cho. of all.	*The Fools are only,* &c.
	Enter Venus.
Venus.	Calms appear, when Storms are past;
	Love will have his Hour at last:
	Nature is my kindly Care;
	Mars destroys, and I repair;
	Take me, take me, while you may,
	Venus comes not ev'ry Day.
Cho. of all.	*Take her, take her,* &c.
Chronos.	The World was then so light,
	I scarcely felt the Weight;
	Joy rul'd the Day, and Love the Night.
	But since the Queen of Pleasure left the
	Ground,
	I faint, I lag,
	And feebly drag
	The pond'rous Orb around.

Momus.   All, all, of a piece throughout;

Pointing }
to *Diana.* }   Thy Chase had a Beast in View;

to *Mars.*   Thy Wars brought nothing about;

to *Venus.*   Thy Lovers were all untrue.

Janus.   'Tis well an Old Age is out,

Chro.   And time to begin a New.

Cho. of all. *All, all, of a piece throughout;*
               Thy Chase had a Beast in View;
               Thy Wars brought nothing about;
               Thy Lovers were all untrue.
               'Tis well an Old Age is out,
               And time to begin a New.
                    Dance of Huntsmen, Nymphs,
                    Warriours and Lovers.

[*The Pilgrim,* 1700]

LXXXIX

The Fair Stranger.
By Mr. DRYDEN.

I

Happy and free, securely blest,
No Beauty cou'd disturb my Rest;
My Amorous Heart was in Despair
To find a new Victorious Fair.

2

'Till you descending on our Plains,
With Forrain Force renew my Chains.
Where now you rule without Controul,
The mighty Soveraign of my Soul.

3

Your Smiles have more of Conquering Charms,
Than all your Native Countries Arms;
Their Troops we can expel with Ease
Who vanquish only when we please.

4

But in your Eyes, oh! there's the spell
Who can see them, and not Rebell?
You make us Captives by your stay,
Yet kill us if you go away.

[*A New Miscellany of Original Poems*, 1701]

XC

THE
LADY's SONG.
By Mr. *DRYDEN.*

1

A Quire of bright Beauties in Spring did appear,
To chuse a *May*-Lady to govern the Year:
All the Nymphs were in White, and the Shepherds in
    Green,

SONG LXXXIX. [British Museum: Harl. MS. 1264, ff. 78ᵛ–80]

The Garland was giv'n, and *Phillis* was Queen:
But *Phillis* refus'd it, and sighing did say,
I'll not wear a Garland while *Pan* is away.

2

While *Pan*, and fair *Syrinx*, are fled from our Shore,
The Graces are banish'd, and Love is no more:
The soft God of Pleasure that warm'd our Desires,
Has broken his Bow, and extinguish'd his Fires;
And vows that himself, and his Mother, will mourn,
'Till *Pan* and fair *Syrinx* in Triumph return.

3

Forbear your Addresses, and Court us no more,
For we will perform what the Deity swore:
But if you dare think of deserving our Charms,
Away with your Sheephooks, and take to your Arms;
Then Lawrels and Myrtles your Brows shall adorn,
When *Pan*, and his Son, and fair *Syrinx*, return.

[*Poetical Miscellanies: the Fifth Part*, 1704]

XCI

A
SONG.
Written by Mr. *DRYDEN*:

I

Fair, sweet and young, receive a Prize
Reserv'd for your Victorious Eyes:
From Crowds, whom at your Feet you see,

O pity, and distinguish me;
As I from thousand Beauties more
Distinguish you, and only you adore.

2

Your Face for Conquest was design'd,
Your ev'ry Motion charms my Mind;
Angels, when you your Silence break,
Forget their Hymns to hear you speak;
But when at once they hear and view,
Are loath to mount, and long to stay with you.

3

No Graces can your Form improve,
But all are lost unless you love;
While that sweet Passion you disdain,
Your Veil and Beauty are in vain.
In pity then prevent my Fate,
For after dying all Reprives too late.

[*Poetical Miscellanies: the Fifth Part,* 1704]

XCII

SONG.
By the same Hand.

I

High State and Honours to others impart,
    But give me your Heart:
That Treasure, that Treasure alone
    I beg for my own.
So gentle a Love, so fervent a Fire
    My Soul does inspire.
That Treasure, that Treasure alone
    I beg for my own.

2

Your Love let me crave,
    Give me in Possessing
    So matchless a Blessing,
That Empire is all I wou'd have.

3

Love's my Petition,
All my Ambition;
If e'er you discover
So faithful a Lover,
So real a Flame,
I'll die, I'll die,
So give up my Game.

    [*Poetical Miscellanies: the Fifth Part*, 1704]

An AYRE on a Ground.

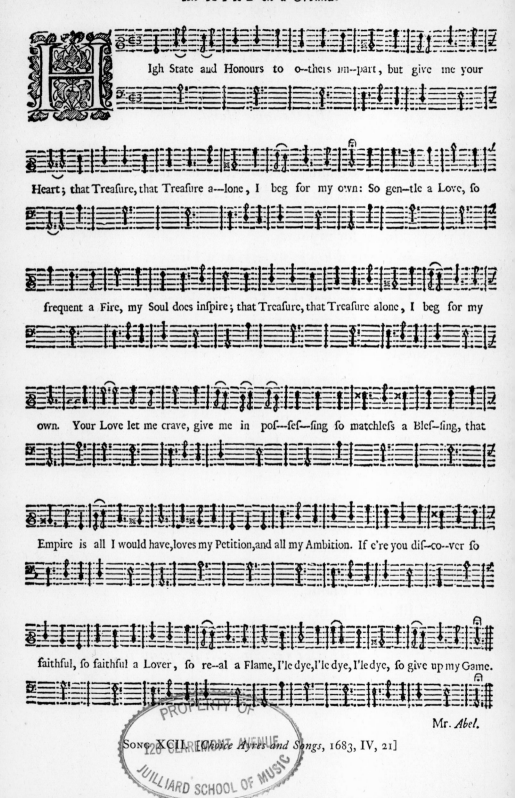

Igh State and Honours to o--thers im--part, but give me your

Heart; that Treasure, that Treasure a---lone, I beg for my own: So gen--tle a Love, so

frequent a Fire, my Soul does inspire; that Treasure, that Treasure alone, I beg for my

own. Your Love let me crave, give me in pos---ses---sing so matchless a Bles--sing, that

Empire is all I would have, loves my Petition, and all my Ambition. If e're you dis--co--ver so

faithful, so faithful a Lover, so re--al a Flame, I'le dye, I'le dye, I'le dye, so give up my Game.

Mr. *Abel*.

SONG XCII. [*Choice Ayres and Songs*, 1683, IV, 21]

NOTES

TEXTUAL NOTES

THE songs in this edition have been reprinted from the earliest authoritative texts, and the original punctuation and spelling have been retained, except that the old-fashioned long "s" and the use of "u" for "v" and "VV" for "W" have been given up in favor of present-day practise. Other textual alterations that have been permitted are the following:

(1) Stanzas are numbered uniformly by means of arabic numerals, whereas in the original texts roman numerals are sometimes used, and stanzas are sometimes unnumbered.

(2) In early editions of seventeenth-century plays, songs are usually printed in italics, proper names (ordinarily italicized) being in roman type. In the present edition, this procedure is reversed: the songs are printed in roman type, the proper names in italics.

(3) Stage directions have been omitted except in the case of *The Secular Masque* (pp. 123–127), where they have seemed essential to an understanding of the author's meaning.

(4) Marginal designations of the characters who sing the songs are retained only in the case of dialogues and part-songs. On p. 13, l. 9, the name *"Ferdinand"* has been supplied in order to indicate the singer of the line.

(5) The title of the ode on the death of Purcell (p. 112) is from the title-page of the first edition.

(6) A few obvious errors of spelling, punctuation, word order, and the like have been corrected. These are recorded in the ensuing list, the first form under each entry representing the corrected reading, the second form the original reading. The five corrections on p. 70 are supplied in a list of errata on sig. ci^v of the first edition of the play; several others are tacitly derived from later editions of Dryden's works.

P. L.
5, 17. In their] In the
6, 12. than] then
9, 16. will I] I will

10, 18. breathe] breath
21, 14. 'em] e'm
24, 9. fainter,] fainter,,
32, 2. lose] loose
34, 21. Than] Then
35, 19. wretched] wretch'd
48, 2. puts] put
      3. aloud] a loud
53, 22. *1.* Lajus! *2.* Lajus! *3.* Lajus!] *1* Lajus! *2* Lajus!
          3 Lajus!
     23. *1.* Hear! *2.* Hear! *3.* Hear!] *1* Hear! *2* Hear! *3* Hear!
58, 9. 1 Farewell] Farwell
     10. Farewell] Farwell
60, 2. your] our
70, 3. Sea-raceing] Sea-spouting
      3. train'd] tam'd
      3. Motion] motion
      6. off] of
      7. unattending] unattended
78, 19. Joys;] Joys
79, 1. improving,] improving.
83, 27. I call] *2.* I call
86, 9. Green-Sward] Green-Sword
113, 17. know] knew
122, 17. Charms] Charm
124, 8. *Chronos*] *Chronus*
     12. Cho] Co
131, 16. receive] reccive

The most authoritative texts of Dryden's songs are the first
editions of his separately published odes and the first editions
of the plays and miscellanies in which his other songs were published. In general, therefore, I have not attempted to collate
subsequent editions and manuscript copies with the texts which
I have used. In the first edition of *Amphitryon* and in the first
edition of the ode on the death of Henry Purcell, however, the
words of each song are printed twice — first by themselves, and
then with the music; and wholly apart from the repetitions de-
manded by the exigencies of the music, several variants have
crept in. Again, it is impossible definitely to determine in
which of four miscellanies "Farewell, fair Armeda" first ap-

peared. Finally, "High state and honors" was first published anonymously as early as 1683 in the fourth volume of *Choice Ayres and Songs*; but I have reprinted the more authoritative text found in the fifth part of *Poetical Miscellanies*, 1704. In these instances, accordingly, I have listed the variants which affect the order of the words or the meaning of the text. Abbreviations are employed as follows, and the first form under each entry represents the reading of the text used in this edition.

WW   *Windsor-Drollery*, 1672
CG   *Covent Garden Drolery*, 1672
WD   *Westminster-Drollery*, 1672
SA   *The Songs in Amphitryon, with the Musick*, 1690 (appended to the first edition of the play)
OP   *An Ode, on the Death of Mr. Henry Purcell*, 1696 (the text accompanying the music)
CA   *Choice Ayres and Songs*, Vol. IV, 1683

P. L.

36, 11. fair *Armeda*] WW my *Almeda* CG fair *Arminda*
    12. I have] WD have I
    12. find] WW found CG hope WD hope
    13. Vertue] WW Honour
    15. my Honour] WW honour
    16. A Fate] WW My fall CG The Fate WD The Fate
    17. were to find] WW or to pine
    18. speediest] WD speedier
38, 1. On Seas] CG Or Seas
    1. in Bullets] WW through bullets
    3. gave me] CG gave
    4. My Fate] WW My fall CG My fall
    5. should] WW would WD would
    6. should] WW would CG would WD would
    7. The Wound on my Breast when] WW When the wound on my brest
    8. You'll] WW You will WD You'd
79, 10. Pleasures] SA pleasure
    14. Then I] SA I then
80, 7. Fair] SA For
    7. love] SA sigh
    7. I dye] SA dye
    10. For I am as false, and as fickle as she] SA O these are the Virtues that Captivate me

80, 18. equally] SA easily
81, 4. Shepherd's] SA happy
82, 7. kiss] SA give
12. Kiss me not] SA doe not kiss
113, 2. lay] OP Lays
10. God-like] OP matchless
18. Tun'd their jarring Sphere] OP turn'd the jarring Spheres
133, 5. fervent] CA frequent
14. All] CA and all

GENERAL NOTES

I. "You twice Ten Hundred Deities." (P. 3.)

From *The Indian-Queen*, 1665, act III. Sung by Ismeron. Dryden and Sir Robert Howard joined forces to write *The Indian-Queen*, and their respective contributions cannot be readily disentangled. The "incantation scene," however, in which this and the next song occur, resembles a similar scene in the second act of *The Indian Emperour*, and therefore seems likely to be Dryden's. The play was acted early in 1664 (A. Nicoll, *A History of Restoration Drama*, 1923, p. 365), and first printed in Howard's *Four New Plays*, 1665. It was later turned into an opera and produced at the Theater Royal, with music by Henry and Daniel Purcell, probably after April, 1695 (W. B. Squire, "Purcell's Dramatic Music," *Sammelbände der Internationalen Musikgesellschaft*, 1904, V, 528–530). The operatic version remained for long unprinted, but there is an early manuscript copy, with the names of some of the actors, in the British Museum (Addit. MS. 31449, ff. 1–69). E. J. Dent edited the opera for the Purcell Society in 1912 (*The Works of Henry Purcell*, 1912, XIX, 1–110).

The present song or incantation was probably recited rather than sung in the original performance. Later it became well known as *The Conjuror's Song, or The Croaking of the Toad*, and it can be found with Purcell's music in *Deliciae Musicae*, 1696, IV, 11–14; *Orpheus Britannicus*, 1698, I, 25–28; 1706, I, 29–34; *ca.* 1745, pp. 19–20; *A Collection of the most Celebrated Songs & Dialogues composed by ye late famous Mr. Henry Purcell, ca.* 1705, pp. 20–21 (it is here said to have been sung by Leveridge); *Mr Henr. Purcell's Favourite Songs, ca.* 1725, Nos. 28, 29; in several collections of single songs in the British Museum [H. 1601. (537); G. 151. (193); G. 304. (191)]; and, according to Squire (*loc. cit.*), in *The Songs in the Indian Queen*, 1695. The words alone, without the music, can be found in *The Hive, ca.* 1733, III, 19; *The Vocal Miscellany*, 1734, II, 88; 1738, II,

61; *The Choice*, 1737, I, 91–92; and *The Aviary, ca.* 1750, pp. 642–643.

II. "Poor Mortals that are clog'd with Earth below." (P. 4.)

From *The Indian-Queen*, 1665, act III. According to the stage directions, the "Song is suppos'd sung by Aerial-Spirits." The passage in which this and the preceding song occur resembles a similar incantation passage in *The Indian Emperour*, and therefore seems likely to be Dryden's.

III. "You to whom Victory we owe." (P. 4.)

From *The Indian-Queen*, 1665, act V. Sung by a priest at the opening of the last act. There is no way of telling, apparently, whether the song is by Dryden or by Howard.

IV. "I look'd and saw within the Book of Fate." (P. 5.)

From *The Indian Emperour, or, The Conquest of Mexico by the Spaniards*, 1667, act II. Sung by Kalib, who "*ascends all in White in the shape of a Woman*," and, after the song is over, descends again. The original music is lost. The play was revived in 1691 (W. B. Squire, "Purcell's Dramatic Music," *Sammelbände der Internationalen Musikgesellschaft*, 1904, V, 528), Kalib's song being set by Henry Purcell, whose music for it is included in *The Banquet of Musick*, 1691, VI, 14–15; *Orpheus Britannicus*, 1698, I, 10–11; 1706, I, 8–9; *ca.* 1745, p. 6; and *Mr Henr. Purcell's Favourite Songs, ca.* 1725, No. 23. A single-sheet edition of the song examined by Alan Gray (*The Works of Henry Purcell*, 1916, XX, viii) specifies Pate as the singer on the occasion of the 1691 revival. The words are printed in *The Aviary, ca.* 1750, p. 267.

V. "Ah fading joy, how quickly art thou past?" (P. 5.)

From *The Indian Emperour, or, The Conquest of Mexico by the Spaniards*, 1667, act IV. Sung by an Indian woman for the entertainment of "Vasquez, Pizarro, *and other* Spaniards *lying carelessly un-arm'd.*" After the song "*two* Spaniards *arise and Dance a* Saraband *with* Castanieta's." There is an attractive musical setting by the gifted composer Pelham Humphrey in *Choice Ayres, Songs, & Dialogues*, 1675, I, 70–71; 1676, I, 66–67. "I. Tyndall" made a glee for four voices of it in 1785 (British Museum: Addit. MS. 31811, ff. 29–32), and Charles Lucas, Principal of the Royal Academy of Music from 1859 to 1866, set it to music as a madrigal for five voices in 1857 [British Museum: H. 1775. v. (27)]. Texts of the words, none of them authoritative, can be found in *New Court-Songs, and Poems. By R. V. Gent.*, 1672, pp. 113–114; *Methinks the Poor Town has been troubled too long*, 1673, p. 33; 2nd ed., 1673, pp. 50–51; *The Wits Academy*, 1677, pp. 57–58; and *The Hive*, ca. 1733, III, 204.

VI. "I feed a flame within which so torments me." (P. 6.)

From *Secret-Love, or The Maiden-Queen*, 1668, act IV. Sung by Asteria (Mrs. Knep). This exquisite song never attained great popularity, and the music would appear to be irrevocably lost. It was printed in *The New Academy of Complements*, 1671 and 1713, p. 132; and seventeenth- and eighteenth-century manuscript versions can be found respectively in Harl. MS. 3991, ff. 82–82ᵛ, and Harl. MS. 7332, f. 198. In the latter it is called *Grideline, or Secret Love*.

VII. "Make ready fair Lady to night." (P. 9.)

From *Sr Martin Mar-all, or The Feign'd Innocence*, 1668, act IV. The first stanza is sung by Warner and the second by Millicent, after an interruption by Moody. The tune is preserved in two ballad-operas: *The Village Opera*, 1729, air XLV, by Charles Johnson; and *The Chamber-Maid*, 1730, air XXIII, by Edward Phillips. The words are in *The New Academy of Complements*, 1671 and 1713, p. 200; *Westminster-Drollery*, 1671 and 1672, p. 47; and *Windsor-Drollery*, 1672, p. 140.

VIII. "Blind Love to this hour." (P. 10.)

From *Sr Martin Mar-all, or The Feign'd Innocence*, 1668, act V. Sung by Warner for Sir Martin, who pretends to serenade Millicent. This is an adaptation of a song by Voiture, as Scott points out (*The Works of John Dryden*, 1808, III, 72). Dryden has reproduced Voiture's meter, and his first, second, fourth, and fifth stanzas are based upon the first, second, seventh, and fourth stanzas of his model. His third stanza is original. Voiture's lines, as found in *Les Oeuvres de Monsieur de Voiture*, 1652, part II (*Poesies*), pp. 61–63, run as follows:

L'Amour sous sa loy
N'a jamais eu d'Amant plus heureux que moy;
Benit soit son flambeau,
Son carquois, son bandeau,
Je suis amoureux,
Et le Ciel ne voit point d'Amant plus heureux.

Mes jours & mes nuits,
Ont bien peu de repos & beaucoup d'ennuis;
Je me meurs de langueur,
J'ay le feu dans le cœur,
Je suis amoureux,
Et le Ciel ne voit point d'Amant plus heureux.

Mortels déplaisirs,
Qui venez traverser mes justes desirs,
Je ne crains point vos coups,
Car, enfin, malgré vous,
Je suis amoureux, &c.

A tous ses martyrs,
L'Amour donne en leurs maux de secrets plaisirs;
Je cheris ma douleur,
Et dedans mon mal-heur,
Je suis amoureux, &c.

Les yeux qui m'ont pris,
Payeroient tous mes maux avec un soûris,
Tous leurs traits me sont doux,
Mesme dans leur couroux,
Je suis amoureux, &c.

Cloris eut des Cieux,
En naissant, la faveur & l'amour des Dieux,
Je la veux adorer,
Et sans rien esperer,
J'en suis amoureux, &c.

Souvent le dépit,
Peut bien, pour quelque temps, changer mon esprit,
Je maudis sa rigueur,
Mais au fond de mon cœur,
J'en suis amoureux, &c.

Estant dans les fers,
De la belle Cloris, je chantay ces vers;
Maintenant d'un sujet,
Mille fois plus parfait,
Je suis amoureux, &c.

La seule beauté,
Qui soit digne d'amour, tient ma liberté,
Et je puis desormais
Dire mieux que jamais,
Je suis amoureux,
Et le Ciel ne voit point d'Amant plus heureux.

Dryden's song is printed in *The New Academy of Complements,* 1671 and 1713, pp. 150–151.

IX. "Where does proud Ambition dwell?" (P. 11.)

From *The Tempest, or The Enchanted Island,* 1670, act II. This and the following songs from *The Tempest* present all the problems of divided authorship that we have encountered in the case of *The Indian-Queen.* Davenant and Dryden collaborated in *The Tempest,* and it was produced in 1667, though not published until 1670. Four years later Shadwell turned the comedy as Dryden and Davenant had left it into an opera, with music by the well-known composer Matthew Lock; and still later Purcell wrote music for a revival of Shadwell's alteration. The complications arising from these successive revisions are many, but they have been skilfully unraveled by W. B. Squire ("Purcell's Dramatic Music," *Sammelbände der Interna-*

tionalen Musikgesellschaft, 1904, V, 551–555) and W. J. Lawrence ("Did Thomas Shadwell Write an Opera on 'The Tempest'?" *Anglia*, 1904, XXVII, 205–217). A volume entitled *The Ariel's Songs in the Play Call'd the Tempest, ca.* 1675, contains music by John Banister, James Hart, and Pelham Humphrey for a production subsequent to 1667 — perhaps for the production of 1674. For further discussion of these knotty matters, see Squire's illuminating article on "The Music in Shadwell's 'Tempest'" in *The Musical Quarterly*, 1921, VII, 565–578, and Lawrence's revision of his earlier essay in the first volume of *The Elizabethan Playhouse*, 1912, pp. 193–206.

The present dialogue was sung by two devils, and it was considerably expanded by Shadwell in 1674. It is impossible to determine whether it is the work, as it stands, of Dryden or of Davenant; though one would be inclined to suspect, were it not for the fact that the preface is signed by Dryden, that Davenant was responsible for nearly the whole alteration. That Dryden was capable of workmanship quite as slovenly, however, is demonstrated by his opera *Albion and Albanius* and his dramatization of *Paradise Lost*.

X. "Around, around, we pace." (P. 12.)

From *The Tempest, or The Enchanted Island*, 1670, act II. Sung by Pride, Fraud, Rapine, and Murther "*in a round encompassing the Duke.*" After singing they dance and then vanish. In Shadwell's revision these lines are utilized as the concluding chorus of a longer song.

XI. "Dry those eyes which are o'reflowing." (P. 13.)

From *The Tempest, or The Enchanted Island*, 1670, act III. Sung by "Ariel *invisible.*" This song was set by Banister, and can be found with his music in *The Ariel's Songs in the Play Call'd the Tempest, ca.* 1675, No. 2, and in Addit. MS. 29396, f. 112^v, dating from about 1680. Shadwell retained the lines in his revision of the play in 1674, and they were furnished with music by Purcell for a still later revival. His setting has been reprinted in *The Works of Henry Purcell*, ed. E. J. Dent, 1912, XIX, 136–143.

XII. "Go thy way." (P. 13.)

From *The Tempest, or The Enchanted Island*, 1670, act III. This dialogue between Ferdinand and Ariel was also set by Banister, and is contained in *The Ariel's Songs in the Play Call'd the Tempest*, ca. 1675, No. 3. The words alone are printed in *Windsor-Drollery*, 1672, pp. 12–13.

XIII. "We want Musick, we want Mirth." (P. 17.)

From *The Tempest, or The Enchanted Island*, 1670, act III. Sung by Caliban.

XIV. "Hark, my *Damilcar*, we are call'd below!" (P. 17.)

From *Tyrannick Love, or The Royal Martyr*, 1670, act IV. "Nakar *and* Damilcar *descend in Clouds, and sing*," and when they have finished, "*The Clouds part*, Nakar *flies up, and* Damilcar *down*." An early anonymous setting, dated June 8, 1681, is preserved in Addit. MS. 19759, ff. 29ᵛ–30, and there is a parody of the dialogue in *The Rehearsal*, 1672, act V, in which the two kings of Brentford appear in the clouds. Purcell's music, composed for a revival of the play about 1695, is included in *Deliciae Musicae*, 1695, I, 16–23; *Orpheus Britannicus*, 1698, I, 148–154; 1706, I, 113–119; ca. 1745, pp. 69–72; *Harmonia Anglicana*, ca. 1765, pp. 74–77; a collection of single songs in the British Museum [H. 1994. a. (118)]; and *The Works of Henry Purcell*, ed. Alan Gray, 1917, XXI, 135–145. In the revival for which Purcell's music was composed, Damilcar was called Daridcar, and the duet was sung, according to *Deliciae Musicae*, by Mr. Bowman and Mrs. Ayliff.

XV. "You pleasing dreams of Love and sweet delight." (P. 21.)

From *Tyrannick Love, or The Royal Martyr*, 1670, act IV. Sung by Damilcar. The music is not extant.

XVI. "Ah how sweet it is to love." (P. 21.)

From *Tyrannick Love, or The Royal Martyr*, 1670, act IV.
Sung by Damilcar. "*At the end of the Song a Dance of Spirits.*"
This song, long deservedly popular, was set to music by Purcell
for the revival of *Tyrannick Love* in 1695. It was sung on that
occasion by Mrs. Ayliff. Purcell's music is printed with the
first two of Dryden's stanzas in *Deliciae Musicae*, 1695, I, 6–7;
Mr Henr. Purcell's Favourite Songs, ca. 1725, No. 2; *Orpheus
Britannicus*, ca. 1745, p. 2; and in several collections of single
songs in the British Museum [K. 7. i. 2. (22); G. 304. (15);
G. 315. (14); and others]. *Orpheus Britannicus*, 1698 and 1706,
I, 3, has only the first stanza of the words. There is an early
eighteenth-century manuscript of Purcell's air in the British
Museum (Addit. MS. 22099, f. 59), and a modern reprint in
The Works of Henry Purcell, ed. Alan Gray, 1917, XXI, 146–
147. The words alone can be found in *Windsor-Drollery*, 1672,
p. 41; *The Hive*, 1732, I, 146; *The Vocal Miscellany*, 1734, II,
233–234; 1738, II, 192–193; *A Complete Collection of Old and
New English and Scotch Songs*, 1735, II, 83; *The Choice*, 1737,
I, 185; *The Aviary*, ca. 1750, pp. 37–38; *The Charmer*, 1752 and
1782, I, 219–220; *The Muses Delight*, 1754, p. 274; *A Collection
of Songs*, 1762, p. 57; and *The Buck's Bottle Companion*, 1775,
p. 57.

XVII. "You charm'd me not with that fair face." (P. 23.)

From *An Evening's Love, or The Mock-Astrologer*, 1671,
act II. Sung by Wildblood (Mr. Hart). The song is preceded
by the following lines:

Wild. Or let us encourage one another to a breach by the dangers
of possession: I have a Song to that purpose.
Jac. Pray let me hear it: I hope it will go to the tune of one of our
Passa-calles.

A *passacaglia*, or *passacaglio*, is "An old Italian or Spanish
dance tune, resembling the chaconne, in slow three-four measure, usually with divisions on a ground base" (*Webster's New
International Dictionary*).

XVIII. "After the pangs of a desperate Lover." (P. 24.)

From *An Evening's Love, or The Mock-Astrologer*, 1671, act II. Sung by Wildblood (Mr. Hart), who prefaces his singing with the remark: "Strike up Gentlemen; we'll entertain 'em with a song *al' Angloise*, pray be ready with your *Chorus*." Doralice in *Marriage A-la-Mode*, 1673, III, i, alludes to Wildblood's song. A setting by Alphonso Marsh the elder is printed in *Choice Songs and Ayres for One Voyce*, 1673, I, 8; *Choice Ayres, Songs, & Dialogues*, 1675 and 1676, I, 4; and a later setting by John Ernest Galliard, a German-born musician who died in England in 1749, is printed in *The Merry Musician*, ca. 1728, II, 87–88, and *The Musical Miscellany*, 1729, I, 100–101. The words of the song can be found in *Merry Drollery Complete. The First Part*, 1670 and 1691, pp. 171–172; *The New Academy of Complements*, 1671 and 1713, pp. 191–192; *Windsor-Drollery*, 1672, p. 139; *The Hive*, ca. 1733, III, 202; 1732, IV, 143; *The Vocal Miscellany*, 1734, II, 130; 1738, II, 98–99; *The Cupid*, 1736, p. 179; 1739, p. 200; and *A Complete Collection of Old and New English and Scotch Songs*, 1736, IV, 42.

XIX. "Calm was the Even, and cleer was the Skie." (P. 26.)

From *An Evening's Love, or The Mock-Astrologer*, 1671, act IV. Sung by Beatrix (Mrs. Knep). A musical setting by Alphonso Marsh can be found in *Choice Songs, and Ayres for One Voyce*, 1673, I, 9; *Choice Ayres, Songs, & Dialogues*, 1675 and 1676, I, 8; and *Wit and Mirth: or Pills to Purge Melancholy*, 1699, 1707, and 1714, I, 177–178; 1719, III, 160–161. The words alone are in *The New Academy of Complements*, 1671 and 1713, pp. 192–193 (with the addition of two spurious stanzas); *Windsor-Drollery*, 1672, p. 100; *The Canting Academy*, 1673, pp. 184–185 (with the addition of two spurious stanzas); *The Compleat Courtier*, 1683, pp. 14–15; *Merry Drollery Compleat. The Second Part*, 1691, pp. 220–221 and 292; *The Masque*, ca. 1790, p. 212; and *The Bagford Ballads*, ed. J. W. Ebsworth,

1878, II, 499–502 (with the addition of eight spurious stanzas). A seventeenth-century manuscript version is preserved in the British Museum (Harl. MS. 3991, ff. 149–149ᵛ).   In *Covent Garden Drolery*, 1672, pp. 38–39, there is an imitation of Dryden's song, beginning "Fair was my Mistress, and fine as a Bride"; and in *Mock Songs and Joking Poems*, 1675, pp. 129–130, there is a song headed *A Mock to, Calm was the Evening and cleer was the Skye*, beginning "Sharp was the Air, and cold was the Ground."

XX.   "*Celimena*, of my heart."   (P. 28.)

From *An Evening's Love, or The Mock-Astrologer*, 1671, act V.   Sung by Wildblood (Mr. Hart) and Jacintha (Mrs. Gwyn).   The original air is lost, but there is an eighteenth-century setting by Dr. Pepusch, celebrated for his overtures in *The Beggar's Opera*, in *The Merry Musician*, ca. 1731, III, 34–35, and *The Musical Miscellany*, 1731, V, 177–179.   The words can be found in *The New Academy of Complements*, 1671 and 1713, p. 106; *Westminster-Drollery*, 1671 and 1672, pp. 30–31; *Windsor-Drollery*, 1672, pp. 101–102; *The Hive*, ca. 1733, III, 209–210; and Harl. MS. 3991, ff. 89–90, dating from the seventeenth century.   There are two burlesques of the dialogue in *Mock Songs and Joking Poems*, 1675, pp. 107–108 and 133. The first, of five stanzas, begins "Pretty Peggy grant to me," and the second, of four stanzas, begins "*Moll*, I nere yet knew my mind."

XXI.   "Beneath a Myrtle shade."   (P. 30.)

From *The Conquest of Granada by the Spaniards*, part I, 1672, act III.   In the first edition this is printed after the epilogue, with the marginal note, "*Misplac'd. Sung at the dance, or Zambra in the third* Act."   John Banister's music is contained in *Choice Songs and Ayres for One Voyce*, 1673, I, 45; *Choice Ayres, Songs, & Dialogues*, 1675 and 1676, I, 37; and *Wit and Mirth: or Pills to Purge Melancholy*, 1699, 1707, and 1714, I, 184–186; 1719, III, 170–171.   The words are in *Westminster-*

Drollery, 1671, pp. 31–33 and 116–117; 1672, pp. 31–33; *Windsor-Drollery,* 1672, p. 5; *The Hive,* 1732, I, 157–158; and *The Aviary, ca.* 1750, p. 78.

XXII. "Wherever I am, and whatever I doe." (P. 32.)

From *The Conquest of Granada by the Spaniards,* part I, 1672, act IV. There are four early musical settings for this song. The first, by Alphonso Marsh, is in *Choice Songs and Ayres for One Voyce,* 1673, I, 37; *Choice Ayres, Songs, & Dialogues,* 1675 and 1676, I, 29; and *Wit and Mirth: or Pills to Purge Melancholy,* 1699, 1707, 1714, I, 180–181; 1719, III, 163–165. The second is by Pelham Humphrey. It has been printed from an unspecified source by John Stafford Smith in *Musica Antiqua,* 1812, II, 170, and it is also available in *The Minstrelcy of England,* ed. A Moffat and F. Kidson, 1901, p. 67 and in *Ten Seventeenth Century Songs,* ed. Sir F. Bridge, n.d., pp. 26–27. A third air is found in a single-sheet edition in the British Museum [G. 313. (163)], and is anonymous; and a fourth, by "Mr. Froud," is in *Calliope, ca.* 1738, I, 105. The words are in *The New Academy of Complements,* 1671 and 1713, pp. 296–297 (in the 1671 edition incorrectly numbered 286–287); *Westminster-Drollery,* 1671 and 1672, pp. 10–11; *Windsor-Drollery,* 1672, pp. 162–163 (incorrectly numbered 138–139); *The Wits Academy,* 1677, pp. 122–123; *The Hive,* 1732, I, 231–232; *The Cupid,* 1736, p. 106; 1739, pp. 119–120; *The Aviary, ca.* 1750, p. 603; *The Charmer,* 1782, II, 153; *A Collection of Songs, Chiefly Such as are Eminent for Poetical Merit,* 1782, p. 153; and a manuscript in the British Museum dating from about 1675 (Sloane MS. 1487, ff. 4–4ᵛ).

XXIII. "How unhappy a Lover am I." (P. 35.)

From *Almanzor and Almahide, or, The Conquest of Granada,* part II, 1672, act IV. Music for the dialogue by Nicholas Staggins is preserved in *Choice Songs and Ayres for One Voyce,* 1673, I, 38; *Choice Ayres, Songs, & Dialogues,* 1675 and 1676, I, 32; *Wit and Mirth: or Pills to Purge Melancholy,* 1699, 1707, and 1714, I, 182–183; 1719, III, 166–167; and in a manuscript in the British Museum dating from about 1680 (Addit. MS. 29396, f. 67ᵛ). The words can be found in *The New Academy of Complements*, 1671 and 1713, pp. 316–317 (in the 1671 edition incorrectly numbered 306–307); *Westminster-Drollery*, 1671 and 1672, pp. 14–15 (the tune is here said to be "*How severe is forgetful old age*"); *Windsor-Drollery*, 1672, pp. 1–2; and *The Hive*, 1732, I, 144–145. There is a six-stanza imitation of the dialogue in *Holborn-Drollery*, 1673, pp. 48–50, entitled *Concealed Love. A Song* and beginning "How unhappy a Lover am I, Whilst the flames in my brest I conceal."

XXIV. "Farewel, fair *Armeda*, my Joy and
my Grief." (P. 36.)

From *New Court-Songs, and Poems. By R. V. Gent.*, 1672, pp. 78–79. This song was never acknowledged by Dryden, and its authenticity is therefore conjectural. It first appeared almost simultaneously in four miscellanies the precise dates of which are unfortunately impossible to determine: *Westminster-Drollery*, 1672, p. 125; *Covent Garden Drolery*, 1672, p. 16; *Windsor-Drollery*, 1672, p. 146; and R. V.'s collection (from which I have taken the present text). Three years later it was ridiculed in the third edition of *The Rehearsal*, 1675, in two passages which, because they have sometimes been misinterpreted, I shall quote in full. In the first passage (II, i) Bayes undertakes to explain the circumstances attendant upon the composition of his poetry, and says:

If I am to write familiar things, as Sonnets to *Armida*, and the like, I make use of Stew'd Prunes only; but, when I have a grand design in hand, I ever take Phisic, and let blood.

Later (III, i) fair Armeda is again brought to the fore:

Bayes. . . . What, are they gone, without singing my last new Song? 'Sbud, would it were in their Bellies. I'll tell you, Mr. *Johnson*, if I have any skill in these matters, I vow to gad, this Song is peremtorily the very best that ever yet was written: you must know, it was made by *Tom Thimble's* first wife after she was dead.
Smi. How, Sir? after she was dead?

Bayes. Ay, Sir, after she was dead. Why, what have you to say to that?

Johns. Say? Why, nothing: he were a Devil that had anything to say to that?

Bayes. Right.

Smi. How did she come to dye, pray Sir?

Bayes. Phoo! that's no matter; by a fall: but here's the conceit, that upon his knowing she was kill'd by an accident, he supposes, with a Sigh, that she dy'd for love of him.

Johns. I, I, that's well enough: let's hear it, Mr. *Bayes*.

Bayes. 'Tis to the Tune of Farewel, fair *Armida*, on Seas, and in battels, in Bullets, and all that.

SONG.

> In swords, Pikes, and Bullets, 'tis safer to be,
> Than in a Strong Castle, remoted from thee:
> My deaths-bruise pray think you gave me, tho a fall
> Did give it me more, from the top of a wall;
> For then if the Moat on her mud would first lay,
> And after before you my body convey:
> The blew on my brest when you happen to see,
> You'l say, with a Sigh, there's a True blew for me.

Ha, Rogues! when I am merry, I write these things as fast as hops, I gad.

This is sheer nonsense, certainly, and to take Tom Thimble and his wife seriously is beside the point; for the general tenor of the passage, despite the contradictory nature of some of the remarks, is clear. The author of this portion of *The Rehearsal*, that is to say, was of the opinion that Dryden wrote "Farewell, fair Armeda," and that it was a poor enough piece of work to justify his ridicule.

It is possible to allege, of course, that the song was foisted upon Dryden with malice prepense, but the usual satirical method of the authors of *The Rehearsal* does not bear out this hypothesis. Nor is it quite legitimate to argue that the song is unworthy of Dryden, and that therefore he could not have written it. Malone, who first printed it as Dryden's (*The Critical and Miscellaneous Prose Works of John Dryden*, 1800, I, i, 104), was definitely of the opposite opinion; and Scott, who also considered it authentic (*The Works of John Dryden*, 1808, XI, 161–162), thought well enough of it to quote the first two lines of the second stanza in *The Pirate*, chapter XXXIX, in connection with the farewell which Captain Cleveland wrote to Minna Troil.   On the other hand, recent editors have very generally rejected the song because, to quote one of them (G. Thorn-Drury, *Covent Garden Drollery*, 1928, p. 128), they see "no real ground for attributing to Dryden" verses which "upon internal evidence no one would have ever imagined to be his." But assuredly the allegation of a contemporary, however hostile, is more reliable evidence than the opinion of a critic, however discriminating and judicial, two hundred and fifty years after the event.

In rejecting Malone's attribution, Mr. Thorn-Drury centers his attack upon the editor of a so-called "key" to *The Rehearsal* (published in 1704), in which fair Armeda is for the first time specifically ascribed to Dryden; but what he has to say in this connection, while sound enough in itself, is hardly relevant to the point at issue. *The Rehearsal*, not the "key" to *The Rehearsal*, should engage our major attention; and even if the editor of the latter had access to no special sources of information, his opinion as a critic in other respects well informed still has a residuum of value.   Mr. Thorn-Drury alludes to what he describes as the "difficulty" that the "parody itself is not to be found in the first edition of *The Rehearsal*," but in a subsequent copy, and he appears to imply that this "difficulty" cannot be satisfactorily disposed of.   But *The Rehearsal* was acted in 1671 before the publication of "Farewell, fair Armeda," and Francis Digby, the supposed subject of the song, was killed in 1672, as Mr. Thorn-Drury admits.

In addition to what appears in *The Rehearsal*, there are one or two suggestions elsewhere to connect Dryden with this song. In *Covent Garden Drolery* there is a song beginning "Farewell, dear *Revechia*, my joy and my grief," in which Revechia has very generally been identified with Dryden's mistress, Mrs. Reeve.   The song is a gross parody of "Farewell, fair Armeda," but it may well have been written to turn the tables on Dryden if the lines on Captain Digby are really his. Also of interest is the fact that "Farewell, fair Armeda" is printed immediately after two indisputable songs of Dryden's in *Choice Songs and Ayres for One Voyce*, 1673, I, 10, and in *Choice Ayres, Songs, & Dialogues*, 1675 and 1676, I, 9. The music for it in these collections is by Robert Smith, a composer who collaborated with Dryden on other occasions. Finally, the fifth line in the last stanza of "Fair, sweet and young, receive a prize" is highly reminiscent of the sixth line in the first stanza of the present song.

"Farewell, fair Armeda" is also found in *The Canting Academy*, 1673, pp. 173–174; Egerton MS. 2623, f. 89 (British Museum); and *The Roxburghe Ballads*, ed. J. W. Ebsworth, 1889, VI, 40–42 (expanded to five stanzas). Usually a reply beginning "Blame not your Armeda nor call her your grief" is printed along with the original words. There is a five-stanza burlesque of the song in *Mock Songs and Joking Poems*, 1675, pp. 79–80, beginning "Far-well my dear Puggy, my Pullet, my Low-bell"; and in the same collection (pp. 7–8) the song "Poor *Arinda* in an Arbour lay sleeping" is to the "*Tune of, Farewell my Armida, my joy.*" The tune is also found as "Farewell, my *Calista*" in *The Village Opera*, 1729, air XLVIII, by Charles Johnson.

XXV. "Why should a foolish Marriage Vow." (P. 38.)

From *Marriage A-la-Mode*, 1673, act I. Sung by Doralice (Mrs. Marshall) and Beliza (Mrs. Slade). This song opens the first act and establishes in effective manner the tone of artificial pastoral beauty that characterizes the rest of the play. It was set by Robert Smith, and is printed with the original music in *Choice Songs and Ayres for One Voyce*, 1673, I, 39; and *Choice Ayres, Songs, & Dialogues*, 1675 and 1676, I, 35. An anonymous eighteenth-century setting appears in *The Musical Miscellany*, 1729, II, 52–53, and *The Merry Musician*, ca. 1735, IV, 161–162. The words can be found in *New Court-Songs, and Poems. By R. V. Gent.*, 1672, p. 72; *The Hive*, 1732, I, 166; *The Nightingale*, 1738, pp. 300–301; *The Aviary*, ca. 1750, p. 617; and *The Tea-Table Miscellany*, 1762, pp. 295–296.

XXVI. "Whil'st *Alexis* lay prest." (P. 40.)

From *Marriage A-la-Mode*, 1673, act IV. Nicholas Staggins composed the music, which was published in *Choice Songs and Ayres for One Voyce*, 1673, I, 27, and *Choice Ayres, Songs, & Dialogues*, 1675 and 1676, I, 22–23. Texts of the words are contained in the following miscellanies: *Covent Garden Drolery*, 1672, p. 62; *New Court-Songs, and Poems. By R. V. Gent.*, 1672, p. 77; *Westminster Drollery, the Second Part*, 1672, pp. 119–120; *The Canting Academy*, 1673, p. 174; *The Wits Academy*, 1677, p. 72; *The Hive, ca.* 1733, III, 201; *The Cupid*, 1736, p. 216; 1739, p. 237; and *The Choice*, 1737, I, 236. The first and last stanzas are preserved in a British Museum manuscript dating from the seventeenth century (Lansd. MS. 740, f. 170ᵛ). There is a rather close imitation of Dryden's song in *Covent Garden Drolery*, 1672, p. 72, and *New Court-Songs, and Poems. By R. V. Gent.*, 1672, pp. 104–105. It begins, in the latter, "So closely, closely prest In his *Clymena's* Arms young *Damon* lay," and it is entitled *Enjoyment. A Song at the King's House.* The "King's House," of course, was the Theater Royal, and the song was doubtless introduced into a contemporary play there in emulation of Dryden's successful entertainment at the theater in Lincoln's Inn Fields.

XXVII. "Eveillez vous, Belles endormies." (P. 42.)

From *The Assignation: or, Love in a Nunnery*, 1673, act II. Sung by Benito (Mr. Haynes). This humorous snatch, one of several bits of song put into the mouth of the tuneful Benito, was perhaps taken from a contemporary French song. Later in the same scene Benito sings the following lines:

> *But still between kissing* Amintas *did say,*
> *Fair* Phillis *look up, and you'll turn night to day.*

XXVIII. "Long betwixt Love and fear *Phillis* tormented." (P. 44.)

From *The Assignation: or, Love in a Nunnery*, 1673, act III. A setting by Robert Smith appears in *Choice Songs and Ayres for One Voyce,* 1673, I, 59, and *Choice Ayres, Songs, & Dialogues,* 1675 and 1676, I, 50; and the words alone are in *London Drollery,* 1673, p. 2; *Methinks the Poor Town has been troubled too long,* 1673, p. 12; 2nd ed., 1673, pp. 34–35; and *The Hive,* 1732, I, 142.

XXIX. "The day is come, I see it rise." (P. 46.)

From *Amboyna,* 1673, act III. Music by Robert Smith, together with the last two stanzas of the text, can be found in *Choice Songs and Ayres for One Voyce,* 1673, I, 60, and *Choice Ayres, Songs, & Dialogues,* 1675 and 1676, I, 47. The last two stanzas of the words are in *Methinks the Poor Town has been troubled too long,* 2nd ed., 1673, p. 9, and all three stanzas are in *London Drollery,* 1673, p. 130, and *The Hive, ca.* 1733, III, 7.

XXX. "Who ever saw a noble sight." (P. 48.)

From *Amboyna,* 1673, act III. This appears in the second edition of *Methinks the Poor Town has been troubled too long,* 1673, pp. 13–14.

XXXI. "Look up, look up, and see." (P. 49.)

From *The State of Innocence, and Fall of Man,* 1677, act III. Before the song begins, according to the stage directions, spirits dance about a tree "*in deform'd shapes,*" and "*after the Dance an Angel enters, with a Woman, habited like* Eve." After line 16, "*The Angel takes the fruit and gives to the Spirits, who danc'd, they immediately put off their deform'd shapes, and appear Angels.*" After line 20, "*The Angel gives to the Woman who eats,*" and after line 25, "*The spirits who are turn'd Angels fly up, when they have tasted.*" Following the song, "*Two Angels descend, they take the Woman each by the hand, and fly up with her out of sight. The Angel who sung, and the Spirits who held the Canopy at the same instant, sink down with the Tree.*"

XXXII. "*Phœbus,* God belov'd by men." (P. 50.)

From *Oedipus,* 1679, act II. Sung by Manto (Mrs. Evans). Dryden and Lee collaborated in *Oedipus,* and the authorship of the *Song to Apollo* is therefore somewhat doubtful. The music is probably irrevocably lost. An early miscellany, *The Compleat Courtier*, 1683, p. 137, has a copy of the words.

XXXIII. "Chuse the darkest part o' th' Grove." (P. 51.)

From *Oedipus*, 1679, act III. Tiresias was acted by Mr. Harris. The present piece was doubtless chanted or recited rather than sung, but I have printed it on account of its essentially lyrical nature. It should be compared with *The Indian-Queen*, III, ii, and *The Indian Emperour*, II, i. The consensus of critical opinion with regard to *Oedipus* seems to be that the whole of the third act, in which also the next song appears, "is beyond all doubt Dryden's" (see *The Works of John Dryden*, ed. Scott and Saintsbury, 1883, VI, 130).

XXXIV. "Hear, ye sullen Pow'rs below." (P. 52.)

From *Oedipus*, 1679, act III. After the second chorus (line 30) there is "A flash of Lightning: the Stage is made bright; and the Ghosts are seen passing betwixt the Trees." At the conclusion of the song, in response to the injunctions of Tiresias, "*The Ghost of* Lajus *rises arm'd in his Chariot, as he was slain. And behind his Chariot, sit the three who were Murder'd with him*." Purcell contributed music for a revival of *Oedipus* in 1692 (W. B. Squire, "Purcell's Dramatic Music," *Sammelbände der Internationalen Musikgesellschaft*, 1904, V, 541), and his setting for the present song has been printed in *The Works of Henry Purcell*, ed. Alan Gray, 1917, XXI, 1–18. Gray (pp. i–ii) lists a number of manuscripts of the music.

XXXV. "Can life be a blessing." (P. 54.)

From *Troilus and Cressida, or, Truth Found too Late*, 1679, act III. The stage directions read: "*Musick. and then Song: during which* Pandarus *listens*." The original music by Thomas Farmer is in *Choice Ayres and Songs*, 1681, III, 3. There is a different setting of later date in *A Collection of Songs . . . Com-*

pos'd by Mr. John Eccles, ca. 1704, p. 137. The words are printed in *The Compleat Courtier*, 1683, p. 130, and *The Hive, ca.* 1733, III, 146. There is a broadside copy of the song in the collection of the Earl of Crawford (*Bibliotheca Lindesiana Catalogue of a Collection of English Ballads*, 1890, No. 201). *Unfeigned Friendship*, a ballad in the Pepys collection, is to the tune of "*Can Life be a Blessing*, &c." (see *The Pepys Ballads*, ed. H. E. Rollins, 1930, III, 82–85).

XXXVI. "'Gainst Keepers we petition." (P. 56.)

From *The Kind Keeper; or, Mr. Limberham*, 1680, act I. Sung by Mrs. Tricksey and Judith. Later texts appeared in *The Hive, ca.* 1733, III, 217, and *The Choice*, 1737, I, 235.

XXXVII. "I my own Jaylour was; my
only Foe." (P. 57.)

From *The Kind Keeper; or, Mr. Limberham*, 1680, act II. Sung by Limberham, probably without musical accompaniment.

XXXVIII. "By a dismal Cypress lying." (P. 57.)

From *The Kind Keeper; or, Mr. Limberham*, 1680, act III. Sung by Judith. I have been unable to find Dryden's professed Italian source. The song appeared in *The Cupid*, 1736, p. 125; 1739, p. 145; and *The Hive, ca.* 1733, III, 207.

XXXIX. "Look down, ye bless'd above, look
down." (P. 58.)

From *The Spanish Fryar or, The Double Discovery*, 1681, act I. The stage directions before the song call for "*A Procession of Priests and Choristers in white, with Tapers, follow'd by the Queen and Ladies . . . the Choristers singing.*" The original music is lost, but incidental music by John Eccles, evidently intended for a revival of the play about 1700, is preserved in Addit. MS. 29378, ff. 139–139ᵛ, with the title *Procession in ye: Spanish Fryar. Mr. John Eccles.*

XL. "Farewell ungratefull Traytor." (P. 58.)

From *The Spanish Fryar or, The Double Discovery*, 1681, act V. Sung by Teresa (Mrs. Crofts). Captain Pack, an obscure musician of little skill, composed the original melody, which can be found in a manuscript dating from about 1681 (Addit. MS. 19759, f. 20ᵛ), and in *Wit and Mirth: or Pills to Purge Melancholy*, 1707 and 1709, IV, 122–123; 1719, V, 334–335. A later setting, ascribed to Thomas Waters, was published about 1780 by I. F[entum], and is contained in a collection of single songs in the British Museum [G. 307. (244)]. The words alone are in *Wit and Drollery. Jovial Poems*, 1682, pp. 305–306; *The Compleat Courtier*, 1683, pp. 139–140; *The Hive*, 1732, I, 196; *The Vocal Miscellany*, 1734, II, 198–199; 1738, II, 157–158; *The Cupid*, 1736 and 1739, p. 2; and *The Aviary*, ca. 1750, pp. 154–155. The song was also expanded to ten stanzas and printed as a broadside (*The Roxburghe Ballads*, ed. J. W. Ebsworth, 1889, VI, 21–22). W. Strunk, in his edition of *All For Love and The Spanish Fryar*, 1911, p. 327, notes that Swinburne reproduced the stanzaic pattern of "Farewell, ungrateful traitor" in *The Garden of Proserpine*, and D. Nichol Smith, in *Dryden Poetry & Prose*, 1925, p. 198, observes that Keats made use of the same pattern in his stanzas beginning "In a drear-nighted December."

An anonymous alteration of Dryden's song was sung to a different tune and became almost as popular as the original. As found in a single-sheet edition in the British Museum [G. 307. (186)], it runs as follows:

> *Farewell thou false* Philander,
>   *Since now from me you rove;*
> *and leave me here to wander,*
>   *no more to think of Love:*
> *I must forever languish*
>   *I must forever mourn;*
> *From Love I now am banish'd,*
>   *and shall no more return.*

2.

Farewell deceitful Traytor,
*   Farewell thou perjur'd Swain;*
Let never injur'd Creature,
*   Believe your Vows again:*
The passion you pretended,
*   Was only to obtain;*
For now the Charm is ended,
*   The Charmer you disdain.*

There is another tune in *The Musical Miscellany*, 1729, I, 42–43
(by "Mr. Gouge"), and in Ralph's *The Fashionable Lady*,
1730, air LXI. The words of the alteration appeared in *The
Choice*, 1733, III, 270; *The Hive, ca.* 1733, III, 135; *The Cupid*,
1736, p. 18; 1739, pp. 15–16; *The Nightingale*, 1738, p. 292;
and *The Aviary, ca.* 1750, p. 157.

XLI. "*Malicorn, Malicorn, Malicorn*, ho!" (P. 60.)

From *The Duke of Guise*, 1683, act III. Sung by a "*Spirit
within.*"

XLII. "Tell me *Thirsis*, tell your Anguish." (P. 61.)

From *The Duke of Guise*, 1683, sigg. L3–L4ᵛ. In the first
edition this song is printed with Captain Pack's music at the
end of the play. It was apparently intended to be sung at the
banquet of Malicorne, where the stage directions read, "*After
a Song and Dance, loud knocking at the door.*" Pack's music can
also be found in *Choice Ayres and Songs*, 1683, IV, 80–81;
Addit. MS. 29397, ff. 25–26ᵛ; and Addit. MS. 19759, ff. 44ᵛ–45.
Both of these manuscripts date from before 1690. The words of
the song are in *Wits Cabinet*, 1703, pp. 132–133; *The Hive*, 1732,
I, 217; and *The Aviary, ca.* 1750, p. 462.

XLIII. "On a bank, beside a Willow." (P. 64.)

From *Miscellany Poems*, 1684, pp. 308–309. Except for the
doubtful "Farewell, fair Armeda," this is the earliest of Dryden's songs not specifically intended for one of his plays. Two

eighteenth-century musical settings have survived — one by James Oswald, a claimant for the honor of having been responsible for the present form of *God Save the King*, and the other by William Boyce, one of the most popular composers of the century. The former may be found in *Universal Harmony*, 1745 and 1746, p. 95, and there is a single-sheet edition in the British Museum [I. 530. (118)]. Boyce's tune, with the first two stanzas only of the words, was also published separately [British Museum: G. 310. (197)]. The words alone appeared in all editions of the first part of *Miscellany Poems* (1692, pp. 301–302; 1702, pp. 170–171; 1716, pp. 102–103; and 1727, p. 97); in Dryden's posthumous *Poems on Various Occasions*, 1701, p. 202; *The Hive*, 1733, II, 13–14; *The Choice*, 1733, II, 48; *The Vocal Miscellany*, 1734 and 1738, I, 249; *A Complete Collection of Old and New English and Scotch Songs*, 1735, I, 134; *The Muses Delight*, 1754, p. 315 (two stanzas only); and *The Tea-Table Miscellany*, 1762, p. 246.

XLIV. "Cease, *Augusta*! Cease thy mourning." (P. 66.)

From *Albion and Albanius*, 1685, act I. Sung by Mercury. *Albion and Albanius* was composed by Louis Grabu, a French musician of mediocre talent, and, contrary to the ordinary custom in operas of the period, the dialogue was set to music throughout. The ten passages here reprinted, therefore, represent merely "*The Songish Part*," to use a term coined by Dryden in his preface, as distinguished from "The recitative part of the *Opera*." It will be noted that three of the "songs" included by Warton in *The Poetical Works of John Dryden*, 1811, II, 370–372, have been rejected as belonging to the latter category rather than to the former. The problem of extracting independent lyrical passages from a work like *Albion and Albanius*, as a matter of fact, is one of considerable difficulty, and there has been little or no uniformity in the practise of previous editors of Dryden's non-dramatic works. Not one of them, surprisingly enough, has printed the lines beginning "From the low palace of old Father Ocean," which in my opinion are among the most quotable in the opera. Dryden himself suggests "softness and variety of Numbers" as a distinguishing characteristic of "*The Songish Part*" of the opera; but a safer basis of selection seems to me to be the literary form of each passage, and it is on this that I have chiefly depended in choosing the extracts printed in the present edition.

Albion and Albanius was performed in June, 1685, after the death of Charles II, who was to have been the chief object of Dryden's allegorical flattery. Grabu's music was contemptuously received, and the opera was a failure, though it is said to have lasted six nights. A sumptuous edition of the complete score was issued in 1687, but modern opinion concurring with that of Grabu's contemporaries, the music has not been reprinted. In 1696 George Powell produced *A New Opera; Called, Brutus of Alba: or, Augusta's Triumph* (published 1697), in which there are extensive borrowings from *Albion and Albanius*. Brutus stands for William III, who was as unctuously exalted by Powell as Charles II and the Duke of York had been by Dryden in the characters of Albion and Albanius. Powell did not scruple to borrow specific lines as well as his general scheme from Dryden's opera. For example, he altered Mercury's admonitions to Augusta (London) as follows:

> Mer. Cease, *fair* Augusta, *cease thy Sorrow,*
> *And tho' to Day thou mourn'st, thou'lt smile to Morrow.*
> *Thy Morning Prayer, and Evening Dreams,*
> *Thy* Albion *with his smiling Beams,*
> *Returns so Glorious, Bright and Gay,*
> *He Rivals the Great God of Day.*

XLV. "Then Zeal and Common-wealth infest." (P. 66.)

From *Albion and Albanius*, 1685, act II. Sung by Albion.

XLVI. "All Hail yee Royal pair!" (P. 67.)

From *Albion and Albanius*, 1685, act II. Sung by Apollo, who appears in the clouds holding the reins of his horses, "*with the Rays and a great glory*" about him. Compare Powell's *Brutus of Alba*, 1697, IV, ii:

Apollo.   Albion *all Hail! Thou Sacred Head!*
Heavens Darling Care, no Danger dread:
For Walls of Fate, thy Life Enclose,
The Plots of thy Malitious Foes,
Abhor'd above, Expos'd below,
Their own dull Light shall shew
Treason, which her Infernal Train
Works in her Hellish Mines in vain.

Chorus.   Albion, all Hail, &c.

Apollo.   *My Oracles declare, When he has done*
His finish'd Work of Fate,
And broke the Universal Yoke,
A Smiling Race of Years, his Reign shall Crown.

XLVII. "Old Father Ocean calls my Tyde." (P. 68.)

From *Albion and Albanius*, 1685, act II. Sung by Thames.
Compare Powell's *Brutus of Alba*, 1697, IV, ii:

Thamesis.   *Hark, I am call'd; old Father Ocean*
Calls my Tide;
Come away.
On the Mounting Billows dancing,
See the Royal Bark advancing;
The Waves, the Wind and Sea,
Are all at Albion's *dear Devotion.*

1st Triton.   *See the Merry Boatswain too,*
Has call'd his Jolley Crew,

Chorus.   Come, come, come, &c.

A Dance of Six Watermen.

Neptune.   *See, see, the Sea Gods trim thy Sails,*
Every Nymph in all her Pride.
1st Triton.   *Wafted by the Calmer Gales,*
O're thy own Main Triumphant Ride.
Augusta.   *Each Neried does her Locks adorn,*
And every Triton minds his Horn:
The Lovely Mermaid too, behold
How she Combs her flowing Gold:
Without a Snare, or Charm, she sings,
Welcome to the best of Kings.

Chorus.   Welcome, &c.

XLVIII. "Yee Nymphs, the Charge is Royal." (P. 68.)

From *Albion and Albanius*, 1685, act II. Sung by "*Two Nymphs and* Triton." After each stanza a "*Chorus of Nymphs and* Tritons *repeat the same Verses*;" and in conclusion the chorus sings the last stanza of the preceding song (*i. e.* the seven lines beginning "See the God of Seas attends Thee"). A chaconne, or Spanish dance in slow triple time, is performed during the progress of the song. Compare Powell's *Brutus of Alba*, 1697, act V:

Fame.	*You Nymphs that attend the Soveraign Barge,* *Guard, guard your Royal Charge;* *And let your loyal Hands the Bark support,* *With all the Glory of your Watry Court.*
Chor.	*Then let your Royal,* &c.
Fame.	*Pleasure and Joy shall waft him o'er,* *And Triumph eccho round from Shore to Shore.*
Grand Chor.	*Pleasure and Joy,* &c.

XLIX. "From the low Palace of old Father Ocean." (P. 70.)

From *Albion and Albanius*, 1685, act III. Sung by Nereids, who rise out of the sea, while Tritons dance.

L. "*Albion*, lov'd of Gods and Men." (P. 70.)

From *Albion and Albanius*, 1685, act III. Sung by Proteus. Compare Powell's *Brutus of Alba*, 1697, act V:

Proteus.	Albion, *belov'd of Earth and Heaven,* *Bid rough War and Battel cease;* *Return with Fame when thou hast driven* *The hunted* Tyrant *down, and given* Europe *a Universal Peace.*
Chor.	Albion *belov'd,* &c.
Proteus.	Albion! Albion! *Heaven attends him;* *Heaven its Guardian-Angels lends him:* *Nor wonder Heaven's best Smile defends him,* *When for Heaven his Sword he draws,* *His Standard's Heaven, and Heaven's his Cause.*

LI. "*Albion*, Hail; The Gods present Thee." (P. 71.)

From *Albion and Albanius*, 1685, act III. Sung by Venus. During the first stanza, "*Graces and Loves, Dance an Entry*," and during the second stanza, "*the Hero's Dance is perform'd*."

LII. "*Sylvia* the fair, in the bloom of Fifteen." (P. 72.)

From *Sylvae: or, The Second Part of Poetical Miscellanies*, 1685, pp. 464–466. There is a setting by William Boyce in *The Merry Musician*, ca. 1735, IV, 3–4; *Calliope, ca.* 1738, I, 187; and in a collection of single songs in the British Museum [G. 305. (138)]. An anonymous Latin translation of "Mr. *Dryden's* pleasing and noted Song" was published by Motteux in *The Gentleman's Journal*, September, 1693, pp. 309–310. Texts of the words, in some cases with the addition of a spurious fourth stanza, are to be found in the following collections: *Sylvae: or, The Second Part of Poetical Miscellanies*, 1692, pp. 280–282; 1702, pp. 150–152; *The Second Part of Miscellany Poems*, 1716, p. 253; 1727, p. 249; Dryden's *Poems on Various Occasions*, 1701, pp. 190–191; *Wit's Cabinet, ca.* 1699, pp. 150–151 (four stanzas); *The Compleat English Secretary*, 1714, pp. 142–143 (four stanzas); *The Cupid*, 1736, p. 185; 1739, pp. 205–206; *A New Academy of Complements*, 1748, pp. 118–119 (four stanzas); and *The Aviary, ca.* 1750, p. 458.

LIII. "Go tell *Amynta* gentle Swain." (P. 73.)

From *Sylvae: or, The Second Part of Poetical Miscellanies*, 1685, pp. 467–468. Several musical settings are extant. The earliest, by Robert King, is in *The Theater of Music*, 1685, I, 30; and *Wit and Mirth: or Pills to Purge Melancholy*, 1700, 1707, and 1712, II, 258; 1719, IV, 301–302. Another, by Henry Purcell, is in a manuscript dating from as early as 1686 (Addit. MS. 30382, ff. 36–37^v); *Orpheus Britannicus*, 1706, I, 263–265; *ca.* 1745, pp. 109–110; and *The Works of Henry Purcell*, ed. W. B. Squire and J. A. Fuller-Maitland, 1922, XXII, 133–136. In 1760 it was printed to an anonymous air in *The Universal Magazine*, 1760, XXVII, 261–262. Later in the century James

Elliott turned the song into a glee for four voices (Addit. MS. 31804, ff. 70–72^v), and Maria Hester Park, precocious daughter of a noted oboist, who made her first public appearance as a singer at the age of seven, made a glee of it for three voices (Addit. MS. 31807, ff. 90^v–91^v). The words of the song are printed in *Sylvae: or, The Second Part of Poetica Miscellanies*, 1692, pp. 283–284; *The Second Part of Miscellany Poems*, 1716, pp. 367–368; 1727, p. 363; Dryden's *Poems on Various Occasions*, 1701, p. 191; *The Hive*, 1733, II, 20; *The Vocal Miscellany*, 1734, II, 308–309; 1738, II, 263; *The Aviary, ca.* 1750, p. 195; and *The Charmer*, 1782, II, 189–190.

LIV. "From Harmony, from heav'nly
Harmony." (P. 75.)

From the broadside edition, "Printed for *T. Dring*, in *Fleet-street.* 1687." Giovanni Battista Draghi composed the original music, but his work was eclipsed by Händel's celebrated setting of later date. Draghi's manuscript is in the library of the Sacred Harmonic Society and names twelve singers: Turner, Abell, Boucher, Robart, Marsh, Church, Freeman, Gosling, Woodson, James Hart, Bowman, and Williams. There is another seventeenth-century manuscript of Draghi's music in the British Museum (Addit. MS. 33287, ff. 221^v–229^v). Among editions of Händel's music may be cited that of the German Händelgesellschaft, Leipzig, 1866. For information relative to the performance of the ode, see W. H. Husk, *An Account of the Musical Celebrations on St. Cecilia's Day*, 1857, pp. 21–24. Scott (*The Works of John Dryden*, 1808, XI, 168) regarded *The Faerie Queene*, II, ix, 22, as a possible source for the latter part of Dryden's first stanza, and Saintsbury in his reprint of Scott's edition (1885, XI, 170) notes that the words "Groundwork for a Song on St. Cecilia's Day" are written in Dryden's copy of *The Fairie Queene*, VII, vii, 12, preserved at Trinity College, Cambridge. Franz Harder ("Eine Deutsche Anregung zu Drydens 'Alexander's Feast'?" *Englische Studien*, 1926, LXI, 177–182) cites a curious parallel to the reference to Jubal in a poem by Jakob Vogel printed in Daniel Georg Morhof's

Unterricht von der teutschen Sprache und Poesie, 1682. Dryden's words can be found in *Examen Poeticum: Being the Third Part of Miscellany Poems*, 1693, pp. 242–246; Dryden's *Poems on Various Occasions*, 1701, pp. 195–197; *Deliciae Poeticae*, 1706, pp. 93–95; *The Hive*, 1733, II, 87–89; and *The Bagford Ballads*, ed. J. W. Ebsworth, 1878, II, 811–813. Tom D'Urfey's ode for the 1691 feast (*Wit and Mirth: or Pills to Purge Melancholy*, 1719, I, 70–71) is indebted to Dryden's ode for the 1687 feast in a number of particulars. The following lines are especially reminiscent of Dryden's third stanza:

> And first the Trumpets Part
> Inflames the Heroe's Heart;
> The Martial Noise compleats his Joys,
> And Soul Inspires by Art:
> And now he thinks he's in the Field,
> And now he makes the foe to yield;
> Now Victory does eagerly pursue,
> And Music's warlike Notes make every fancy true.

LV. "What shall I do to show how much I
love her?" (P. 78.)

From *The Prophetess: or, The History of Dioclesian*, 1690, act III. The authenticity of this song is doubtful. Langbaine (*An Account of the English Dramatick Poets*, 1691, p. 214) ascribes *The Prophetess*, an opera made out of Fletcher and Massinger's play of the same name, to Dryden. But Gildon (*The Lives and Characters of the English Dramatick Poets*, 1699, p. 60) specifically contradicts Langbaine's statement and gives the alteration to Betterton. Downes (*Roscius Anglicanus*, 1708, p. 42) furnishes independent evidence in support of Gildon. The notion that Dryden somehow had a hand in the work has nevertheless persisted. Certainly he contributed a prologue, and Professor Saintsbury (*The Works of John Dryden*, 1884, VIII, 10) is of the opinion that "the lyric insertions, which are neither voluminous, nor specially remarkable, sometimes have a flavour of him." Mr. Norman Ault, who prints the present song in his *Seventeenth Century Lyrics*, 1928, pp. 430–431, appears to hold a similar view, as does Mr. R. G. Ham in an interesting letter to *The Times Literary Supplement*, Thursday, October 8, 1931, p. 778. It should be added, however, that if the "late *Opera*" mentioned by Dryden in the preface to *Amphitryon* was *The Prophetess* (and it is reasonable to suppose that it was), the probability that he was connected with the authorship of it is greatly diminished. For a judicial summary of the claims of Betterton, see A. C. Sprague, *Beaumont and Fletcher on the Restoration Stage*, 1926, pp. 69–71. It is also highly significant that two songs from *The Prophetess* ("Let monarchs fight" and "Let the soldiers rejoice") are ascribed to Betterton in the contemporary *Joyful Cuckoldom, ca.* 1695, Nos. 1 and 2, and that Dryden does not mention *The Prophetess* in the accurate catalogue of his plays prefixed to the first edition of *King Arthur*, 1691.

The present song, like the other lyrical portions of the opera, was composed by Henry Purcell. It appears with his music in *Wit and Mirth: or Pills to Purge Melancholy*, 1700, 1707, and 1712, II, 293–294; 1719, IV, 234–235; Addit. MS. 35043, f. 11; Addit. MS. 30303, f. 8ᵛ; and *The Works of Henry Purcell*, ed. Sir F. Bridge and J. Pointer, 1900, IX, 63–66. The tune was also utilized in *The Beggar's Opera*, 1728, air VI, and *The Jew Decoy'd*, 1735, air VIII. Texts of the words can be found in *Wit's Cabinet, ca.* 1699, p. 152; *The Compleat Academy of Complements*, 1705, p. 141; *The Compleat English Secretary*, 1714, p. 143; *A New Academy of Complements*, 1715, p. 144; *The Hive, ca.* 1733, III, 84; *The Vocal Miscellany*, 1734 and 1738, I, 114–115; *A Complete Collection of Old and New English and Scotch Songs*, 1735, I, 51; *The Cupid*, 1736, p. 121; 1739, p. 137; *The Choice*, 1737, I, 97; *A New Academy of Compliments*, 1743, pp. 140–141; 1748, p. 119; 1789, p. 100; and *The Aviary, ca.* 1750, p. 555.

LVI. "*Celia*, that I once was blest." (P. 79.)

From *Amphitryon; or, The Two Socia's*, 1690, act III. Purcell's music was originally published with the first edition of the play in a supplement entitled *The Songs in Amphitryon*, *with the Music,* 1690, pp. 1–2, and it has been edited for the Purcell Society by Alan Gray (*The Works of Henry Purcell,* 1906, XVI, 31). The words and music can also be found in *Joyful Cuckoldom, ca.* 1695, No. 17 (Bowman is specified as the singer); *Wit and Mirth: or Pills to Purge Melancholy,* 1700, 1707, and 1712, II, 303–304; 1719, IV, 257–258; and Addit. MS. 22099, f. 44, dating from about 1705. The words alone can be found in *The Compleat Academy of Complements,* 1705, pp. 131–132 (with the addition of a spurious fourth stanza); *The Compleat English Secretary,* 1714, pp. 125–126; *A New Academy of Complements,* 1715, pp. 139–140; *The Hive,* 1732, I, 126; *The Cupid,* 1736, p. 64; 1739, p. 72; *A New Academy of Compliments,* 1748, p. 108; *ca.* 1750 and 1784, pp. 134–135; 1789, p. 90. Expanded to ten stanzas it was published as a broadside ballad by C. Bates under the title of *Coy Celia's Cruelty,* a copy being preserved in the Earl of Crawford's collection (*Bibliotheca Lindesiana Catalogue of a Collection of English Ballads,* 1890, No. 208). Among ballads that were sung to the tune of "Celia, that I once was blest" may be mentioned *The False-hearted Lover* and *The Young-Mans Lamentation* (*The Pepys Ballads,* ed. H. E. Rollins, 1931, VII, 149–156), and *Constant Cloris* [British Museum: C. 39. k. 6. (23)]. The tune was also used by Chetwood in *The Lover's Opera,* 1729, air XII.

LVII. "Fair *Iris* I love, and hourly I dye." (P. 80.)

From *Amphitryon; or, The Two Socia's,* 1690, act IV. The part of Mercury was originally played by Lee. Purcell's music was first published in *The Songs in Amphitryon, with the Musick,* 1690, pp. 3–4 (appended to the first edition of the play), and it is here that the corrupt first line, "For Iris I sigh and hourly die," which was usually adopted in later texts, first established itself. The words and music are also printed in *Joyful Cuckoldom, ca.* 1695, No. 18; in *Wit and Mirth: or Pills to Purge Melancholy,* 1700, 1707, and 1712, II, 305; 1719, IV, 246–247; and, edited by Gray, in *The Works of Henry Purcell,*

1906, XVI, 32–33. An altered version, with music by the popular composer James Hook, was "Sung by Mr. Dubellamy at Marybone Gardens" in 1774. One single-sheet edition of this version in the British Museum [G. 307. (247)] begins "For Polly I sigh," and another [H. 1994. b. (21)] begins "For Sally I sigh." The former consists of only two stanzas. The words of Dryden's song appear without the music in *A New Academy of Complements*, 1715, p. 139; *The Hive*, 1732, I, 56; *The Vocal Miscellany*, 1734, II, 257; 1738, II, 205–206; *The Cupid*, 1736, p. 150; 1739, p. 175; *The Nightingale*, 1738, p. 134; *The Aviary*, ca. 1750, p. 155; *The London Songster*, 1773, pp. 395–396; and *The Masque*, ca. 1790, p. 91. The British Museum [C. 39. k. 6. (48)] has an edition of the song expanded to eight stanzas and published by C. Bates as a broadside ballad.

LVIII. "Fair *Iris* and her Swain." (P. 81.)

From *Amphitryon; or, The Two Socia's*, 1690, act IV. Purcell's music can be found in *The Songs in Amphitryon, with the Musick*, 1690, pp. 5–13 (appended to the first edition of the play); in *Orpheus Britannicus*, 1702 and 1711, II, 153–156; ca. 1745, pp. 107–108; in *Thesaurus Musicus*, ca. 1765, pp. 16–18; and, edited by Alan Gray, in *The Works of Henry Purcell*, 1906, XVI, 34–41. There is a different air entitled "Fair Iris and her swain" in Charles Coffey's ballad-opera *The Female Parson*, 1730, air VII. The words can be found in *The Hive*, ca. 1733, III, 175–176; *A Complete Collection of Old and New English and Scotch Songs*, 1736, III, 35–36; *The Choice*, 1737, I, 118–119; *The Cupid*, 1739, pp. 249–250 (a ten-line chorus is inserted before the last stanza); *The Aviary*, ca. 1750, pp. 158–159; and *The Tea-Table Miscellany*, 1762, pp. 232–234 (among other variations the last stanza is omitted and a spurious stanza inserted in its place). According to an advertisement in *The Daily Courant*, No. 376, Leveridge and Mrs. Campion sang the dialogue of "*Fair* Iris, &c" at a revival of *The Relapse* at Drury Lane, Thursday, July 1, 1703.

LIX. "*Woden*, first to thee." (P. 83.)

From *King Arthur: or, The British Worthy*, 1691, act I. *King Arthur* was composed by Henry Purcell, and was much more successful than Grabu's *Albion and Albanius*. There are two modern reprints of the whole opera, the first edited by Edward Taylor for the Musical Antiquarian Society in 1843, and the second edited by Dennis Arundell for the Purcell Society in 1928 as volume XXVI of *The Works of Henry Purcell*. There is a very full list of the manuscript versions of Purcell's music in Arundell's edition (pp. iii–vi), and references to these are accordingly omitted in the ensuing notes on the individual songs.

The present sacrificial song is intended for four soloists, — a bass, a tenor, an alto, and a soprano, — together with a chorus of priests. The first seventeen lines are printed as a separate song in *Orpheus Britannicus*, 1711, II, 182–183. The last nine lines, from "I call ye all" to the end of the song, are also printed separately in *Orpheus Britannicus*, 1706, I, 231–232, and in a single-sheet edition in the British Museum [H. 1601. (251)]. At a performance of *The School-Boy*, Tuesday, March 28, 1704 (see *The Daily Courant*, No. 608), "The Sacrifice in King *Arthur*" was sung as part of a miscellaneous entertainment of singing and dancing.

LX. "Come if you dare, our Trumpets sound." (P. 84.)

From *King Arthur: or, The British Worthy*, 1691, act I. After a battle "supposed to be given behind the Scenes," the Britons "sing this Song of Triumph." The words and music are in *Joyful Cuckoldom*, ca. 1695, No. 6, and *Wit and Mirth: or Pills to Purge Melancholy*, 1699, 1707, 1714, I, 313; 1719, III, 288–289. The last line of the first stanza is borrowed from the third stanza of *A Song for St. Cecilia's Day*, 1687.

LXI. "Hither this way, this way bend." (P. 85.)

From *King Arthur: or, The British Worthy*, 1691, act II. Two interruptions occur in the song, the first after line 17 and the second after line 23. The stage directions at the latter point read: "*They all incline to* Philidel." Lines 1–23 are printed separately in *Orpheus Britannicus*, 1706, I, 283–286. During the first interruption, and before the song is resumed at line 18, the song beginning "Let not a Moon-born Elf mislead ye" is sung.

LXII. "Let not a Moon-born Elf mislead ye." (P. 86.)

From *King Arthur: or, The British Worthy*, 1691, act II. Sung by Grimbald.

LXIII. "How blest are Shepherds, how happy their Lasses." (P. 87.)

From *King Arthur: or, The British Worthy*, 1691, act II. Sung by a shepherd. The words and music are in *Wit and Mirth: or Pills to Purge Melancholy*, 1699, 1707, 1714, I, 314; 1719, III, 290–291. The words alone are in *The Compleat English Secretary*, 1714, pp. 138–139; *The Hive*, 1732, I, 150; *The Choice*, 1737, I, 75; and *The Aviary*, ca. 1750, p. 227. An expanded version of seven stanzas was published by C. Bates as a broadside ballad about 1691. There is a copy in the British Museum [C. 39. k. 6. (25)]. The tune was used by Drury in his ballad-opera *The Mad Captain*, 1733, air XXVI.

LXIV. "Shepherd, Shepherd, leave Decoying." (P. 88.)

From *King Arthur: or, The British Worthy*, 1691, act II. Sung by two shepherdesses, and intended as an answer to the preceding song. The parts of the shepherdesses were taken by boys with treble voices. The words and music are in *Orpheus Britannicus*, 1706, I, 236–237; the words alone in *The Hive*, 1732, I, 150–151, and *The Choice*, 1737, I, 75–76.

LXV. "We must work, we must haste." (P. 88.)

From *King Arthur: or, The British Worthy*, 1691, act III. Sung by Philidel.

LXVI. "Thus, thus I infuse." (P. 89.)

From *King Arthur: or, The British Worthy*, 1691, act III. Sung by Philidel, who "*approaches* Emmeline, *sprinkling some of the Water over her Eyes, out of the Vial.*"

LXVII. "Oh Sight, the Mother of Desires." (P. 89.)

From *King Arthur: or, The British Worthy*, 1691, act III. The words are printed in *The Hive*, 1732, I, 28, and *The Choice*, 1737, I, 204.

LXVIII. "What ho, thou *Genius* of the Clime, what ho!" (P. 90.)

From *King Arthur: or, The British Worthy*, 1691, act III. With the exception of the last four lines, this is printed with the music in *Orpheus Britannicus*, 1706, I, 275–282, where it is entitled "The Frost Scene in the Third Act of *King Arthur*." The words alone, the last four lines being again omitted, are in *The Hive*, ca. 1733, III, 79–80. The "Frost Music," under which title the song became known, was a popular piece in the early eighteenth century for performance between the acts of stage plays. On Friday, June 30, 1705, for example, according to an advertisement in *The Daily Courant*, No. 1001, it was sung at a revival of *The Royal Merchant*. In 1715 it was sung at thirteen performances of *The Island Princess* by the singers Leveridge, Pack, Cook, Jones, Reading, Mrs. Cross, and Mrs. Cook. Advertisements of these performances appeared on the days when they were to take place in *The Daily Courant*, Nos. 4138, 4139, 4147, 4151, 4157, 4169, 4189, 4195, 4212, 4227, 4353, 4359, and 4397, for January 28 and 29, February 8, 12, and 19, March 5 and 29, April 5 and 25, May 12, October 6 and 13, and November 26. In the following year the "Frost Musick" was again sung by some of the same singers at revivals of *The Island Princess* on March 24, May 10, May 22, and December 17, 1716 (see *The Daily Courant*, Nos. 4501, 4541, 4551, and 4730). Doubtless it was sung at many other revivals which either I have failed to notice or which perhaps were not mentioned in advertisements in the daily journals. The next song was probably included with the "Frost Musick" at these performances.

LXIX. "See, see, we assemble." (P. 92.)

From *King Arthur: or, The British Worthy*, 1691, act III. The last stanza is sung by a chorus of "cold people."

LXX. "Sound a Parley, ye Fair, and surrender." (P. 93.)

From *King Arthur: or, The British Worthy*, 1691, act III. Sung by Cupid. The words and music are in *Thesaurus Musicus*, 1694, II, 27–30; *Orpheus Britannicus*, 1698, I, 159–161; 1706, I, 130–138; *ca.* 1745, pp. 77–78; *A Collection of the most Celebrated Songs & Dialogues composed by ye late famous Mr. Henry Purcell*, *ca.* 1705, pp. 26–27; *Mr Henr. Purcell's Favourite Songs*, *ca.* 1725, Nos. 41, 42; *Harmonia Anglicana*, *ca.* 1765, pp. 46–47; and *Thesaurus Musicus*, *ca.* 1765, pp. 70–71. The words are printed in *The Hive*, 1733, II, 60.

LXXI. "O pass not on, but stay." (P. 93.)

From *King Arthur: or, The British Worthy*, 1691, act IV. According to the stage directions, "*two Syrens arise from the Water; They shew themselves to the Waste, & sing.*" The second part of the song, beginning "Two Daughters of this Aged Stream are we," is printed in *Orpheus Britannicus*, 1698, I, 35–37; 1706, I, 13–15; *ca.* 1745, pp. 9–10; and *Harmonia Anglicana*, *ca.* 1765, pp. 22–23.

LXXII. "How happy the Lover." (P. 94.)

From *King Arthur: or, The British Worthy*, 1691, act IV. The stage directions read: "Nymphs *and* Sylvanus *come out from behind the Trees. Base and two Trebles sing the following Song to a* Minuet. *Dance with the Song, all with Branches in their Hands.*" The words and music of the last four lines of the first stanza are printed in *Orpheus Britannicus*, 1698, I, 45-47; 1706, I, 27-28; *ca.* 1745, p. 18; *Harmonia Anglicana, ca.* 1765, p. 28; in a collection of single-sheet songs in the British Museum [G. 316. (115)]; and without being recognized as Dryden's in *The Works of Henry Purcell*, ed. W. B. Squire and J. A. Fuller-Maitland, 1922, XXII, 118-119. The words of the whole song are printed without the music in *The Hive*, 1732, I, 38.

LXXIII. "Ye Blust'ring Brethren of the Skies." (P. 95.)

From *King Arthur: or, The British Worthy*, 1691, act V. Sung by Aeolus, "*in a Cloud above.*"

LXXIV. "Round thy Coasts, Fair Nymph of *Britain.*"
(P. 96.)

From *King Arthur: or, The British Worthy*, 1691, act V. Sung by Pan and a Nereid.

LXXV. "For Folded Flocks, on Fruitful Plains." (P. 96.)

From *King Arthur: or, The British Worthy*, 1691, act V. Sung by Pan and a Nereid. The words and music are in *Orpheus Britannicus*, 1698, I, 213-215; 1706, I, 195-197; *ca.* 1745, pp. 94-95; *Thesaurus Musicus, ca.* 1765, pp. 2-3; and the words alone are in *The Hive*, 1732, I, 188.

LXXVI. "Your Hay it is Mow'd, & your Corn
is Reap'd." (P. 97.)

From *King Arthur: or, The British Worthy*, 1691, act V. Purcell's music is printed with the words in *Wit and Mirth: or Pills to Purge Melancholy*, 1707 and 1712, III, 223-224; 1719, V, 141-142; and in an early single-sheet edition in the British Museum [G. 304. (188)]. The words are in *The Aviary, ca.* 1750, p. 660. An altered and expanded version, together with an answer, was published as a broadside ballad (*The Roxburghe*

Ballads, ed. W. Chappell, 1880, III, 610). The melody turns up under the title "We've cheated the parson" (from the first line of Dryden's second stanza) in Chetwood's *The Lover's Opera*, 1729, air XXVII; Gay's *Polly*, 1729, air XLVI; *The Jovial Crew*, 1731, air XLVIII; Gay's *Achilles*, 1733, air XVI; Coffey's *The Merry Cobler*, 1735, air I; and *Court and Country*, 1743, air III.

LXXVII. "Fairest Isle, all Isles Excelling." (P. 98.)

From *King Arthur: or, The British Worthy*, 1691, act V. Sung by Venus. Purcell's charming music is printed with the words in *Orpheus Britannicus*, 1698, I, 83 (the first and third stanzas only); 1706, I, 57 (the first and third stanzas only); ca. 1745, p. 34; *Wit and Mirth: or Pills to Purge Melancholy*, 1707 and 1709, IV, 216–217; 1720, VI, 56–57; *The Musical Miscellany*, 1731, VI, 200–201; *Universal Harmony*, 1745 and 1746, p. 109; *The Vocal Enchantress*, ca. 1783, pp. 204–205; and in a single-sheet edition published by R. Falkener about 1775 [British Museum: H. 1994. a. (83)]. In this last it is said to have been sung "by Mrs. Scott, at the Theatre-Royal, Drury Lane," and it consists of but two stanzas. The words of the song are included in *The Hive*, 1732, I, 151; *The Choice*, 1733, III, 272; *The Vocal Miscellany*, 1734, II, 293; 1738, II, 225; *The Nightingale*, 1738, p. 182; *The Aviary*, ca. 1750, p. 155; *The Muses Delight*, 1754, p. 310; *The Charmer*, 1752 and 1782, I, 228; and *The Busy Bee*, ca. 1790, II, 184–185. A two-stanza imitation was quite as popular as Dryden's original song. As found in a single-sheet edition in the British Museum [G. 303. (75)] it is entitled *The Happy Man Set by Mr. Holcombe*, and runs thus:

> *Happy Hours, all Hours excelling,*
>   *when retir'd from crowds and noise:*
> *Happy is that silent dwelling,*
>   *fill'd with self-possessing Joys.*
> *Happy that contented Creature,*
>   *who with fewest things is pleas'd,*
> *And consults ye voice of nature,*
>   *when of roving fancies eas'd.*

> Ev'ry Passion wisely moving,
>   Just as Reason turns the Scale;
> Ev'ry State of Life improving,
>   That no anxious thought prevail:
> Happy Man, who thus possesses,
>   Life, with some Companion dear;
> Joys imparted, still increases,
>   Greifs when told, soon disappear.

Holcombe's tune can also be found in *The Musical Miscellany*, 1730, IV, 166–167, and in *Calliope, ca.* 1738, I, 108. There is a different tune in another single-sheet edition in the British Museum [G. 316. e. (17)]; and the words of the imitation may be found in *The Hive*, 1732, IV, 101; *The Choice*, 1733, III, 233–234; *The Charmer*, 1752 and 1782, I, 270–271; *The Bull-Finch, ca.* 1780, p. 220; and *The Masque, ca.* 1790, p. 97.

LXXVIII.   "St. *George*, the Patron of our Isle." (P. 99.)

From *King Arthur: or, The British Worthy*, 1691, act V. Sung by Honour.

LXXIX.   "No no, poor suff'ring Heart no Change endeavour." (P. 100.)

From *Cleomenes, the Spartan Heroe*, 1692, act II. The words and music can be found in *Comes Amoris*, 1693, IV, 1; *Joyful Cuckoldom, ca.* 1695, No. 19; *Wit and Mirth: or Pills to Purge Melancholy*, 1707 and 1709, IV, 237–238; 1720, VI, 89–90; *The Works of Henry Purcell*, ed. Alan Gray, 1906, XVI, 120–121; and in two early manuscripts in the British Museum (Addit. MS. 35043, f. 5^v; and Addit. MS. 24889, ff. 21^v, 46^v, 66^v, and 89^v). The first of these manuscripts dates from before 1700. In *Joyful Cuckoldom* the singer is said to have been Mrs. Butler. The words of the song can be found in *The Compleat Academy of Complements*, 1705, pp. 116–117; *The Compleat English Secretary*, 1714, pp. 127–128; *A New Academy of Complements*, 1715, p. 141; *The Hive*, 1732, I, 211; and *A New Academy of Compliments*, 1748, pp. 109–110; 1789, pp. 91–92.

LXXX. "Ask not the Cause, why sullen *Spring.*" (P. 101.)

From *Examen Poeticum: Being the Third Part of Miscellany Poems*, 1693, pp. 255–257. A musical setting attributed to John Blow is printed with the first two stanzas of the words in *Mercurius Musicus*, March, 1699, pp. 45–47. There is a different tune in *The Musical Miscellany*, 1730, III, 198–200, and *The Merry Musician*, ca. 1731, III, 151–152. The words are in Dryden's *Poems on Various Occasions*, 1701, p. 194; *The Fifth Part of Miscellany Poems*, 1716, pp. 284–285; 1727, pp. 279–280; *The Hive*, 1733, II, 56; *The Choice*, 1733, III, 26–27; *The Vocal Miscellany*, 1734, II, 158; 1738, II, 123; *A Complete Collection of Old and New English and Scotch Songs*, 1736, IV, 32; *The Aviary*, ca. 1750, p. 35; *The Charmer*, 1782, II, 151–152.

LXXXI. "Creator Spirit, by whose aid." (P. 102.)

From *Examen Poeticum: Being the Third Part of Miscellany Poems*, 1693, pp. 307–309. There are later texts in Dryden's *Poems on Various Occasions*, 1701, p. 197; *Miscellanea Sacra*, 1705, pp. 7–9; and *The Fifth Part of Miscellany Poems*, 1716, pp. 251–252; 1727, pp. 248–249. *Veni Creator Spiritus* is one of the most widely known of mediaeval Latin hymns. Ekkehard ascribed it to Charles the Great, but it is probably not older than the tenth century. An authoritative text is given in Guido Maria Dreves, *Analecta Hymnica*, 1888, II, 93–94. As edited in A. S. Walpole's *Early Latin Hymns*, 1922, pp. 374–376, it reads as follows:

> Veni creator Spiritus,
> mentes tùorum uisita,
> imple superna gratia,
> quae tu creasti pectora:
>
> qui Paraclitus diceris,
> donum Dei altissimi,
> fons uiuus, ignis, caritas,
> et spiritalis unctio.

tu septiformis munere,
dextrae Dei tu digitus,
tu rite promisso Patris
sermone ditas guttura.

accende lumen sensibus,
infunde amorem cordibus,
infirma nostri corporis
uirtute firmans perpeti.

hostem repellas longius,
pacemque dones protinus,
ductore sic te praeuio
uitemus omne noxium.

per te sciamus da Patrem,
noscamus atque Filium,
te utriusque Spiritum
credamus omni tempore.

LXXXII. "*Chloe* found *Amyntas* lying." (P. 105.)

From *Examen Poeticum: Being the Third Part of Miscellany Poems*, 1693, pp. 429–430. The earliest musical setting is by John Gilbert in *Deliciae Musicae*, 1695, II, 2, and *Wit and Mirth: or Pills to Purge Melancholy*, 1699, 1707, and 1714, I, 232–233; 1719, I, 328–329. There is also a setting by John Blow in *Amphion Anglicus*, 1700, pp. 92–100, and the song was printed to a "French air" in *The Vocal Magazine*, 1798, II, No. 102. The words alone are in Dryden's *Poems on Various Occasions*, 1701, p. 186; *The Fifth Part of Miscellany Poems*, 1716, p. 211; 1727, p. 209; *The Choice*, 1733, III, 1–2; *The Vocal Miscellany*, 1734, II, 105; 1738, II, 75–76; *A Collection of Songs*, 1762, p. 176; and *The Buck's Bottle Companion*, 1775, p. 176 (the third stanza and the first, second, fifth, and sixth lines of the second stanza are omitted).

LXXXIII. "What State of Life can be so blest." (P. 108.)

From *Love Triumphant; or, Nature will Prevail*, 1694, act III. Music by John Eccles is contained in *Thesaurus Musicus*, 1694, II, 31; *Joyful Cuckoldom*, ca. 1695, No. 34; and *Wit and Mirth:*

or Pills to Purge Melancholy, 1707 and 1709, IV, 269–270. In all of these collections the singer is said to have been Mrs. Hudson. The words alone are in *Wit and Mirth: or Pills to Purge Melancholy*, 1720, VI, 163; *The Hive, ca.* 1733, III, 215–216; *The Cupid*, 1736, p. 105; 1739, p. 119; and *The Choice*, 1737, I, 80.

LXXXIV. "Young I am, and yet unskill'd." (P. 110.)

From *Love Triumphant; or, Nature will Prevail*, 1694, act V. The music for this song was also composed by Eccles, and may be found with the words in *Thesaurus Musicus*, 1694, II, 2; *The Gentleman's Journal*, January and February, 1694, p. 35 (two stanzas only); *Wit and Mirth: or Pills to Purge Melancholy*, 1699, 1707, and 1714, I, 238; 1719, III, 227–228; and Addit. MS. 35043, f. 6ʳ. The tune appears with other words in Lillo's ballad-opera *Silvia*, 1730, air XX, and Lillo's words were later printed in *The Musical Companion*, 1741, p. 35. The original song can be found without the music in *Wit's Cabinet, ca.* 1699, pp. 146–147; *The Theatre of Ingenuity*, 1704, p. 149 (two stanzas only); *The Compleat Academy of Complements*, 1705, pp. 120–121; *The Compleat English Secretary*, 1714, pp. 121–122; *A New Academy of Complements*, 1715, pp. 132–133; *The Muses Holiday, ca.* 1730, p. 62; *The Hive*, 1732, I, 66; *The Cupid*, 1736, p. 15; 1739, p. 13; *The Choice*, 1737, I, 70–71; *A New Academy of Compliments*, 1748, p. 105; *ca.* 1750 and 1784, p. 141; 1789, p. 87; *The Aviary, ca.* 1750, pp. 654–655; *The Charmer*, 1752 and 1782, I, 201; *The Muses Delight*, 1754, p. 302; and *The Busy Bee, ca.* 1790, II, 177–178.

LXXXV. "Mark how the Lark and Linnet
Sing." (P. 112.)

From the first edition, 1696. The title-page reads:

[within a rule] / AN / ODE, / ON THE / DEATH / OF / Mr. Henry Purcell; / Late Servant to his Majesty, and / Organist of the Chapel Royal, / and of St. *Peter's Westminster.* / [rule] / The Words by Mr. *Dryden*, and Sett to / Musick by Dr. *Blow.* / [double rule] /

LONDON, / Printed by *J. Heptinstall*, for *Henry Playford*, at his Shop / in the *Temple Change Fleetstreet*, or at his House in / *Arundel-street* over against the Blew Ball. 1696.

Dryden's ode is printed on the verso of the title-page in the first edition, and also, with Blow's music, on pp. 1–30. It appears without the music among the prefatory poems in *Orpheus Britannicus*, 1698, I, iv; in *Oxford and Cambridge Miscellany Poems*, ca. 1706, pp. 172–173; and in *The Grove*, 1721, pp. 235–237. Purcell died November 21, 1695. Arthur Bedford, a disciple of Jeremy Collier, attacked the ode as blasphemous in *The Great Abuse of Musick*, 1711, pp. 163–165.

LXXXVI.   "'Twas at the Royal Feast, for *Persia* won."
(P. 114.)

From the first edition, 1697. The title-page reads:

Alexander's Feast; / OR THE / POWER / OF / MUSIQUE. / AN / ODE, / In Honour of / St. CECILIA's Day. / [double rule] / By Mr. *DRYDEN*. / [double rule] / *LONDON*, / Printed for *Jacob Tonson* at the *Judge's Head* near the / *Inner-Temple*-Gate, in *Fleet-street*. 1697.

Alexander's Feast, Dryden's second ode for St. Cecilia's Day, was performed at Stationer's Hall on Monday, November 22, 1697. Jeremiah Clarke's music was not printed. Advertisements in *The Post Boy*, Nos. 405 and 407, announced performances of the ode at Hickford's Dancing School on Thursday, December 9, for the benefit of Clarke and Le Riche, and at York Buildings on Thursday, December 16, for the benefit of Le Riche, who appears from Addit. MS. 35043, ff. 105–106, to have composed an overture for the ode. Purcell's name is ambiguously associated with *Alexander's Feast* in some lines by Dr. Kenrick in *The Grove*, 1721, p. 123:

> Such Bliss we feel, if we but *Purcell* hear,
> We're Transport all, and wish each Pore an Ear:
> Transport, which only can be well exprest,
> In *Dryden's* Words, at *Alexander's* Feast.

Händel's later musical setting has made the song known to many generations of music-lovers, and has often been reprinted, for example by the German Händelgesellschaft, Leipzig, 1862. Without listing the various editions of Händel's work, it may be remarked that the chorus of the first stanza attained a certain vogue as a separate song, and is printed as such in *Calliope*, *ca.* 1739, II, 92–93; *The Muses Delight*, 1754, pp. 110–112; and *Harmonia Anglicana*, *ca.* 1765, pp. 12–15. The words of the whole ode were printed in two little-known miscellanies: *A Select Collection of Modern Poems*, Dublin, 1713, pp. 153–160, and *The Poetical Miscellany*, 1762, pp. 283–290. F. Harder ("Eine Deutsche Anregung zu Drydens 'Alexander's Feast'?" *Englische Studien*, 1926, LXI, 177–182) has suggested that Dryden was influenced in both of his St. Cecilia's Day odes by a war-song ascribed to Jakob Vogel and printed by Daniel Georg Morhof in his *Unterricht von der teutschen Sprache und Poesie*, 1682. Among the lines quoted by Harder, the following are the most remarkable for their similarity in form and content to *Alexander's Feast*:

> Dromml und Pfeiffn gut
> Macht Heldenmuth,
> Erweckt Prophetn,
> Reitzt die Poetn,
> In Fried und Streit,
> Hört mans allzeit,
> Musicam soll man ehren,
> Man kann ihr nicht entbehren.
> Man schreibt, dass wenn Timotheus
> Nach der Dorier weise thet singen:
> Als ein berühmter Musicus
> Kondt er in Harnisch bringen:
> Alexandrum Magnum, den Held,
> Streitts satt kondt er nicht werden,
> Biss er zwang fast die ganze Welt,
> Bekriegt den Kreyss der Erden.
> Timotheus,
> Milesius,
> Kondt gewaltig singn,
> Thet mit auffbringen

Alexandrum,
Regem Magnum
Das er in Wuth
Und Heldenmuth
Fast Schild, Schwert, und Kriegswaffen,
Im Grimm die Feind zu straffen.

LXXXVII. "Look, look, I see — I see my Love appear." (P. 121.)

From *The Pilgrim*, 1700, pp. 43–46. The performance of *The Pilgrim* for which this and the following song were written took place after Dryden's death, probably about April 29 (see A. C. Sprague, *Beaumont and Fletcher on the Restoration Stage*, 1926, pp. 89–93). The stage directions call for "*Musick within*" before the present song commences, and then "*The Lovers enter at Opposite Doors, each held by a Keeper.*" After line 20, "*they break from their Keepers; run to each other, and embrace,*" and at the conclusion of the song, "They run out together hand in hand."

LXXXVIII. "*Chronos, Chronos,* mend thy Pace." (P. 123.)

From *The Pilgrim*, 1700, pp. 47–54. There is a sympathetic interpretation of *The Secular Masque* in Mr. F. W. Bateson's *English Comic Drama 1700–1750*, 1929, pp. 1–3. I have been unable to trace the music for the whole masque, but there is a manuscript in the British Museum (Addit. MS. 29378, ff. 194–205^v) of the part composed by Daniel Purcell. His airs, moreover, were published in a volume entitled *A Collection of New Songs . . . Compos'd by Mr. Daniel Purcel. Perform'd in the Revis'd Comedy call'd the Pilgrim*, 1700, which contains the first, third, fourth, and fifth stanzas. Janus was sung by Freeman, according to this collection, Momus by Pate, and Diana by Mrs. Erwin. The passage sung by Venus beginning "Calms appear when storms are past" was set to music by Gottfried Finger, a German who is said to have left England in disgust when he was awarded the fourth prize in the competition to set

Congreve's *Judgment of Paris* to music in 1701. There is a single-sheet edition in the British Museum [G. 151. (35)] of the song of Venus as it was sung by Mrs. Campion, and it was printed without the music in *A Collection of Songs*, 1762, pp. 76–77, and *The Buck's Bottle Companion*, 1775, pp. 76–77. Other passages were also separately published, Diana's "With horns and with hounds" being especially popular. This came out with Daniel Purcell's music in a single-sheet edition [British Museum: G. 151. (172)], and later, when set by William Boyce, in *A Choice Collection of Favorite Hunting Songs*, ca. 1770, I, 32–33; in a single-sheet edition in the British Museum [G. 313. (259)]; and without the music in *The Wreath*, 1753, p. 201; *A Collection Of Songs*, 1762, p. 203; *The Town and Country Song-Book*, ca. 1770, p. [8] (sung by Miss Poitier at the theater in Covent Garden); *The London Songster*, 1773, p. 383 (sung by Miss Poitier at Covent Garden); *The Buck's Bottle Companion*, 1775, p. 203; *The Bull-Finch*, ca. 1775, p. 34 (sung by Mrs. Vernon at Covent Garden); ca. 1780, p. 101 (sung by Mrs. Baker at Covent Garden); *The Masque*, ca. 1790, p. 241; and *The Busy Bee*, ca. 1790, III, 75. Boyce's *Lyra Britannica*, ca. 1750, pp. 1–9, contains his settings for "With horns and with hounds," "Thy sword within the scabbard keep," and "Calms appear." The first stanza of the masque was published with D. Purcell's music in *Mercurius Musicus*, May, 1700, pp. 31–32, and as a single song [British Museum: G. 315. (154)]. There is a manuscript of a setting by James Hook for "With horns and with hounds" in the library of the Sacred Harmonic Society.

LXXXIX. "Happy and free, securely blest." (P. 127.)

From *A New Miscellany of Original Poems*, 1701, pp. 257–258. Scott (*The Works of John Dryden*, 1808, XI, 163) was of the opinion that these verses were addressed to Louise de la Querouaille. A seventeenth-century manuscript in the British Museum (Harl. MS. 1264, ff. 78ᵛ–80) contains the only musical setting, which is perhaps attributable to Cornelio Galli, a talented Italian who was one of the Gentlemen of the Chapel to Queen Catherine in the time of Charles II.

XC. "A Quire of bright Beauties in Spring did appear." (P. 128.)

From *Poetical Miscellanies: the Fifth Part*, 1704, pp. 182–183. No early musical setting is known, but James Elliott made the song into a glee which is printed in *Orpheus*, 1905, No. 386. Scott (*The Works of John Dryden*, 1808, XI, 175) observed that the "obvious application of this song is to the banishment of King James, and his beautiful consort Mary of Este." This conjecture is supported by the fact that there is a copy of the song headed "*Written by Mr. Dryden, in the Year* 1691" in *The Miscellaneous Works of His Grace George, Late Duke of Buckingham*, 1707, I, 122–123. The words can also be found in *The Fifth Part of Miscellany Poems*, 1716, p. 51; 1727, pp. 50–51; *The Muses Holiday*, ca. 1730, pp. 117–118; *A Complete Collection of Old and New English and Scotch Songs*, 1736, IV, 10; *The Choice*, 1737, I, 161–162; *The Aviary*, ca. 1750, p. 31; and *The Tea-Table Miscellany*, 1762, pp. 273–274.

XCI. "Fair, sweet and young, receive a Prize." (P. 131.)

From *Poetical Miscellanies: the Fifth Part*, 1704, pp. 263–264. The words may be found in *The Fifth Part of Miscellany Poems*, 1716, pp. 118–119; 1727, p. 117; *A Complete Collection of Old and New English and Scotch Songs*, 1736, IV, 159; *The Aviary*, ca. 1750, p. 161; *The Muses Delight*, 1754, p. 317 (the first four lines of the first and third stanzas only); *The Tea-Table Miscellany*, 1762, p. 184 (the first four lines of the first and third stanzas only); and *The Charmer*, 1782, II, 152–153.

XCII. "High State and Honours to others impart." (P. 133.)

From *Poetical Miscellanies: the Fifth Part*, 1704, pp. 265–266. This was set by John Abell, and published as early as 1683 in

Choice Ayres and Songs, 1683, IV, 21. Three manuscripts of about the same date in the British Museum also contain the words and music (Addit. MS. 19759, f. 32^v; Addit. MS. 29397, ff. 8^v–9; Addit. MS. 30303, f. 5^v). The words are printed in *The Second Part of Miscellany Poems*, 1716, pp. 174–175; 1727, p. 171; and *The Fifth Part of Miscellany Poems*, 1716, pp. 119–120; 1727, pp. 117–118.

INDEXES

INDEX OF FIRST LINES

A choir of bright beauties in spring did appear 128

After the pangs of a desperate lover 24

Ah fading joy how quickly art thou past 5

Ah how sweet it is to love . . 21

Albion hail the gods present thee 71

Albion loved of gods and men . 70

All hail ye royal pair 67

Around around we pace . . . 12

Ask not the cause why sullen spring 101

Beneath a myrtle shade . . . 30

Blind love to this hour 10

By a dismal cypress lying . . . 57

Calm was the even and clear was the sky 26

Can life be a blessing 54

Cease Augusta cease thy mourning 66

Celia that I once was blest . . 79

Celimena of my heart 28

Chloe found Amyntas lying . . 105

Choose the darkest part of the grove 51

Chronos Chronos mend thy pace 123

Come if you dare our trumpets sound 84

Creator spirit by whose aid . . 102

Dry those eyes which are o're-flowing 13

Eveillez-vous belles endormies . 42

Fair Iris and her swain . . . 81

Fair Iris I love and hourly I die 80

Fair sweet and young receive a prize 131

Fairest isle all isles excelling . . 98

Farewell fair Armeda my joy and my grief 36

Farewell ungrateful traitor . . 58

For folded flocks on fruitful plains 96

From harmony from heavenly harmony 75

From the low palace of old Father Ocean 70

'Gainst keepers we petition . . 56

Go tell Amynta gentle swain . 73

Go thy way 13

Happy and free securely blest . 127

Hark my Damilcar we are called below 17

Hear ye sullen powers below . . 52

High state and honors to others impart 133

Hither this way this way bend . 85

How blest are shepherds how happy their lasses 87

How happy the lover 94

How unhappy a lover am I . . 35

I feed a flame within which so torments me 6

I looked and saw within the book of fate 5

I my own jailor was my only foe 57

Let not a moon-born elf mislead ye 86

Long betwixt love and fear Phillis tormented 44

Look down ye blest above look down 58

Look look I see I see my love appear 121

Look up look up and see . . . 49

Make ready fair lady to-night . 9
Malicorn Malicorn Malicorn ho 60
Mark how the lark and linnet
sing 112

No no poor suffering heart no
change endeavor 100

O pass not on but stay 93
O sight the mother of desires . . 89
Old Father Ocean calls my tide 68
On a bank beside a willow . . 64

Phœbus god beloved by men . 50
Poor mortals that are clogged
with earth below 4

Round thy coasts fair nymph of
Britain 96

St. George the patron of our isle 99
See see we assemble 92
Shepherd shepherd leave decoy-
ing 88
Sound a parley ye fair and su-
rrender 93
Sylvia the fair in the bloom of
fifteen 72

Tell me Thirsis tell your anguish 61
The day is come I see it rise . . 46
Then zeal and commonwealth
infest 66

Thus thus I infuse 89
'Twas at the royal feast for
Persia won 114

We must work we must haste . 88
We want music we want mirth. 17
What ho thou genius of the clime
what ho 90
What shall I do to show how
much I love her 78
What state of life can be so blest 108
Where does proud Ambition
dwell 11
Wherever I am and whatever I
do 32
Whilst Alexis lay pressed . . . 40
Who ever saw a noble sight . . 48
Why should a foolish marriage
vow 38
Woden first to thee 83

Ye blustering brethren of the
skies 95
Ye nymphs the charge is royal . 68
You charmed me not with that
fair face 23
You pleasing dreams of love and
sweet delight 21
You to whom victory we owe . 4
You twice ten hundred deities . 3
Young I am and yet unskilled . 110
Your hay it is mowed and your
corn is reaped 97

INDEX OF NAMES AND TITLES

Abell, John, 134, 167, 186

Account of the English Dramatick Poets, An, 168

Account of the Musical Celebrations on St. Cecilia's Day, An, 167

Achilles, 177

"Ah, fading joy, how quickly art thou past," vii, ix

Albion and Albanius, ix, xi, 66–71, 146, 162–166, 172

Alexander's Feast, vii, 114, 182, 183

All for Love and The Spanish Fryar, 160

Almanzor and Almahide, 35–37, 151

Amboyna, 46–49, 157

Amphion Anglicus, 180

Amphitryon, ix, x, xi, 79–82, 138, 169–171

Analecta Hymnica, 179

Anglia, 146

Ariel's Songs in the Play Call'd the Tempest, The, 14–16, 146, 147

Arundell, Dennis, 172

Assignation, The, 42, 44, 156

Ault, Norman, 168

Aviary, The, 142, 148, 151, 155, 160, 161, 166, 167, 169, 171, 173, 176, 177, 179, 181, 186

Ayliff, Mrs. (singer), 147, 148

Bagford Ballads, The, 149, 168

Baker, Mrs. (singer), 185

Banister, John, ix, 14–16, 31, 146, 150

Banquet of Musick, The, 142

Bates, C., 170, 171, 173

Bateson, F. W., 184

Beaumont and Fletcher on the Restoration Stage, 169, 184

Bedford, Arthur, 182

Beggar's Opera, The, 150, 169

Betterton, Thomas, ix, x, 168, 169

Bibliotheca Lindesiana Catalogue of a Collection of English Ballads, 159, 170

"Blame not your Armeda nor call her your grief," 155

Blow, John, xi, 103, 179, 180, 182

Boucher (singer), 167

Bowman (singer), 147, 167, 170

Boyce, William, 162, 166, 185

Bridge, Sir Frederick, 151, 169

Brutus of Alba: or, Augusta's Triumph, 163–165

Buck's Bottle Companion, The, 148, 180, 185

Bull-Finch, The, 178, 185

Busy Bee, The, 177, 181, 185

Butler, Mrs. (singer), 178

Calliope, 151, 166, 178, 183

"Calms appear when storms are past," 184, 185

Campion, Mrs. (singer), 171, 185

"Can Life be a Blessing," 159

Canting Academy, The, 149, 155, 156

Catherine of Braganza, 186

"Celia that I once was blest," 170

Chamber-Maid, The, 143

Chappell, William, 177

Charles II, ix, 163, 186

Charles the Great, 179

Charmer, The, 148, 151, 167, 177–179, 181, 186

Chetwood, William Rufus, 170, 177

Choice, The, 142, 148, 156, 159, 161, 162, 169, 171, 173, 174, 177–181, 186

Choice Ayres and Songs, ix, 134, 139, 158, 161, 187

Choice Ayres, Songs, & Dialogues, 8, 143, 149–151, 155–157

Choice Collection of Favorite Hunting Songs, A, 185

Choice Songs and Ayres for One Voyce, 25, 27, 31, 33, 37, 39, 41, 43, 45, 47, 55, 63, 149–151, 155–157
Church (singer), 167
Clarke, Jeremiah, 182
Cleomenes, x, xi, 100, 178
Coffey, Charles, 171, 177
Collection of New Songs . . . Compos'd by Mr. Daniel Purcel, A, 184
Collection of Songs, A, 148, 180, 185
Collection of Songs, Chiefly Such as are Eminent for Poetical Merit, A, 151
Collection of Songs . . . Compos'd by Mr. John Eccles, A, 158
Collection of the most Celebrated Songs & Dialogues composed by ye late famous Mr. Henry Purcell, A, 141, 175
Collier, Jeremy, 182
Comes Amoris, 178
Compleat Academy of Complements, The, 169, 170, 178, 181
Compleat Courtier, The, 149, 158–160
Compleat English Secretary, The, 166, 169, 170, 173, 178, 181
Complete Collection of Old and New English and Scotch Songs, A, 148, 149, 162, 169, 171, 179, 186
Concealed Love. A Song, 152
Congreve, William, 185
Conjuror's Song, or The Croaking of the Toad, The, 141
Conquest of Granada, The, 30–34, 150, 151
Constant Cloris, 170
Cook (singer), 174
Cook, Mrs. (singer), 174
Court and Country, 177
Covent Garden Drolery, 139, 150, 152, 154, 156
Covent Garden Drollery (ed. Thorn-Drury), 154
Coy Celia's Cruelty, 170
Crawford, James Ludovic Lindsay, Earl of, 159, 170
Critical and Miscellaneous Prose Works of John Dryden, The, 153
Crofts, Mrs. (singer), 160

Cross, Mrs. (singer), 174
Cupid, The, 149, 151, 156, 159–161, 166, 169–171, 181

Daily Courant, The, 171, 172, 174
Davenant, William, 145, 146
Deliciae Musicae, 106, 141, 147, 148, 180
Deliciae Poeticae, 168
Dent, E. J., 141, 147
Digby, Francis, Captain, 154, 155
Dorset, Charles Sackville, Earl of, viii
Downes, John, 168
Draghi, Giovanni Battista, xi, 75, 167
Dreves, Guido Maria, 179
Dring, T., 167
Drury, Robert, 173
Dryden, John, vii–xi, 137, 138, 141, 142, 144–146, 148, 150, 152–163, 166–169, 171, 176, 177, 179, 180, 182–184, 186
Dryden Poetry & Prose, 160
Dubellamy (singer), 171
Duke of Guise, The, 60–64, 161
D'Urfey, Thomas, 168

Early Latin Hymns, 179
Ebsworth, J. W., 149, 155, 160, 168
Eccho Song, 15
Eccles, John, x, 109, 111, 159, 180, 181
Ekkehard, 179
Elizabethan Playhouse, The, 146
Elliott, James, 167, 186
Englische Studien, 167, 183
English Comic Drama 1700–1750, 184
Enjoyment. A Song at the King's House, 156
Epithalamium, 46
Erwin, Mrs. (singer), 184
Evans, Mrs. (singer), 157
Evening's Love, An, 23–29, 148–150
Examen Poeticum: Being the Third Part of Miscellany Poems, 101–107, 168, 179, 180

Faerie Queene, The, 167

"Fair Iris and her swain," 171

Fair Stranger, The, 127

"Fair, sweet and young, receive a prize," 155

"Fair was my Mistress, and fine as a Bride," 150

Falkener, R., 177

False-hearted Lover, The, 170

"Farewell, dear *Revechia*, my joy and my grief," 154

"Farewell, fair Armeda, my joy and my grief," x, 138, 153–155, 161

"Farewell, my *Calista*," 155

"Farewell my dear Puggy, my Pullet, my Low-bell," 155

"Farewell thou false *Philander*," 160

"Farewell, ungrateful traitor," 160

Farmer, Thomas, 55, 158

Fashionable Lady, The, 161

Female Parson, The, 171

F[entum], I., 160

Fifth Part of Miscellany Poems, The, 179, 180, 186, 187

Finger, Gottfried, xi, 184

Fletcher, John, x, 168

"For Iris I sigh and hourly die," 170

"For Polly I sigh," 171

"For Sally I sigh," 171

Four New Plays, 141

Freeman (singer), 167, 184

"From the low palace of old Father Ocean," 162

"Frost Music," 174, 175

Froud (composer), 151

Fuller-Maitland, J. A., 166, 176

Galli, Cornelio, 185

Galliard, John Ernest, 149

Garden of Proserpine, The, 160

Gay, John, 177

Gentleman's Journal, The, 111, 166, 181

Gilbert, John, 106, 180

Gildon, Charles, 168

God Save the King, 162

Gosling (singer), 167

Gouge (composer), 161

Grabu, Louis, ix, xi, 162, 163, 172

Gray, Alan, 142, 147, 148, 158, 170, 171, 178

Great Abuse of Musick, The, 182

Grideline, or Secret Love, 143

Grove, The, 182

Gwyn, Mrs. Nell, 150

Ham, Roswell G., 169

Händel, G. F., 167, 183

"Happy Hours, all Hours excelling," 177

Happy Man, The, 177

Harder, Franz, 167, 183

Harmonia Anglicana, 147, 175, 176, 183

Harris (singer), 158

Hart, Charles, 148–150

Hart, James, 146, 167

Haynes, Joseph, 156

"High state and honors to others impart," 139

History of Restoration Drama, A, 141

Hive, The, 141, 143, 148–152, 155–157, 159–162, 167–171, 173–179, 181

Holborn-Drollery, 152

Holcombe, Henry, 177, 178

Hook, James, 171, 185

"How severe is forgetful old age," 152

"How unhappy a Lover am I, Whilst the flames in my brest I conceal," 152

Howard, Sir Robert, 141, 142

Hudson, Mrs. (singer), 109, 181

Humphrey, Pelham, ix, 8, 143, 146, 151

Husk, W. H., 167

"In a drear-nighted December," 160

Indian Emperour, The, vii, x, 5–8, 141, 142, 158

Indian Queen, The, x, 3, 4, 141, 142, 145, 158

Island Princess, The, 174

James II, 163, 186
Jew Decoy'd, The, 169
Johnson, Charles, 143, 155
Jones (singer), 174
Jovial Crew, The, 177
Joyful Cuckoldom, 169, 170, 172, 178, 180
Judgment of Paris, The, 185

Keats, John, 160
Kenrick, Daniel, 182
Kidson, Frank, 151
Kind Keeper, The, 56, 57, 159
King, Robert, 74, 166
King Arthur, x, xi, 83–100, 169, 172–178
Kittredge, G. L., xii
Knep, Mrs. (singer), 143, 149
Knotting Song, The, viii

Lady's Song, The, 128
Langbaine, Gerard, x, 168
Lawrence, W. J., 146
Lee (singer), 170
Lee, Nathaniel, 157
Le Riche (composer), 182
"Let monarchs fight for power and fame," 169
"Let the soldiers rejoice," 169
Leveridge, Richard, 141, 171, 174
Lillo, George, 181
Lines Written at Sea, viii
Lives and Characters of the English Dramatick Poets, The, 168
Lock, Matthew, 145
London Drollery, 157
London Songster, The, 171, 185
Love Triumphant, x, 108–112, 180, 181
Lover's Opera, The, 170, 177
Lucas, Charles, 143
Lyra Britannica, 185

Mad Captain, The, 173
Malone, Edmund, 153, 154
Marriage A-la-Mode, viii, 40–43, 149, 155, 156

Marsh, Alphonso, ix, 25, 27, 33, 149, 151, 167
Marshall, Mrs. (singer), 155
Mary of Modena, 186
Masque, The, 149, 171, 178, 185
Massinger, Philip, x, 168
Mercurius Musicus, 103, 179, 185
Mercury's Song to Phædra, 80
Merry Cobler, The, 177
Merry Drollery Compleat. The Second Part, 149
Merry Drollery Complete. The First Part, 149
Merry Musician, The, 149, 150, 155, 166, 179
Methinks the Poor Town has been troubled too long, 143, 157
Minstrelcy of England, The, 151
Miscellanea Sacra, 179
Miscellaneous Works of His Grace George, Late Duke of Buckingham, The, 186
Miscellany Poems, vii, 65, 161, 162
Mock Songs and Joking Poems, 150, 155
Mock to, Calm was the Evening and cleer was the Skye, A, 150
Moffat, Alfred, 151
"Moll, I nere yet knew my mind," 150
Morhof, Daniel Georg, 167, 183
Motteux, Peter Anthony, 166
Mr Henr. Purcell's Favourite Songs, 141, 142, 148, 175
Muses Delight, The, 148, 162, 177, 181, 183, 186
Muses Holiday, The, 181, 186
Musica Antiqua, 151
Musical Companion, The, 181
Musical Miscellany, The, 149, 150, 155, 161, 177–179
Musical Quarterly, The, 146

New Academy of Complements, A, 166, 169–171, 178, 181
New Academy of Complements, The, 143, 145, 149–152

New Academy of Compliments, A, 169, 170, 178, 181

New Court-Songs, and Poems, 38, 143, 152, 155, 156

New Miscellany of Original Poems, A, 128, 185

Nicoll, Allardyce, 141

Nightingale, The, 155, 161, 171, 177

Ode, on the Death of Mr. Henry Purcell, An, 112, 137–139, 181

Oedipus, 50–54, 157, 158

Oeuvres de Monsieur de Voiture, Les, 144

Orpheus, 186

Orpheus Britannicus, 141, 142, 147, 148, 166, 171–177, 182

Oswald, James, 162

Otway, Thomas, viii

Oxford and Cambridge Miscellany Poems, 182

Pack, Captain, 59, 63, 160, 161, 174

Paradise Lost, 146

Park, Maria Hester, 167

Pastoral Dialogue betwixt Thyrsis and Iris, A, 81

Pate (singer), 142, 184

Pepusch, John Christopher, 150

Pepys Ballads, The, 159, 170

Phillips, Edward, 143

Pilgrim, The, 121–127, 184

Pirate, The, 154

Plain Dealer, The, viii

Playford, John, viii

Poems on Various Occasions, 162, 166–168, 179, 180

Poetical Miscellanies: the Fifth Part, 131–133, 139, 186

Poetical Miscellany, The, 183

Poetical Works of John Dryden, The, 162

Pointer, J., 169

Poitier, Miss (singer), 185

Polly, 177

"Poor *Arinda* in an Arbour lay sleeping," 155

Post Boy, The, 182

Powell, George, 163–165

"Pretty Peggy grant to me," 150

Procession in ye: Spanish Fryar, 159

Prophetess, The, ix, x, 79, 168, 169

Purcell, Daniel, xi, 141, 184, 185

Purcell, Henry, ix–xi, 137, 138, 141, 142, 145–148, 158, 166, 169–172, 177, 182

Querouaille, Louise de la, 185

Ralph, James, 161

Reading (singer), 174

Reeve, Mrs. Anne, 154

Rehearsal, The, x, 147, 152–154

Relapse, The, 171

Robart (singer), 167

Rochester, John Wilmot, Earl of, viii

Rollins, H. E., xii, 159, 170

Rondelay, 105

Roscius Anglicanus, 168

Roxburghe Ballads, The, 155, 160, 176

Royal Merchant, The, 174

"Sacrifice in King *Arthur*, The," 172

Saintsbury, George, x, 158, 167, 168

Sammelbände der Internationalen Musikgesellschaft, 141, 142, 145, 158

School-Boy, The, 172

Scott, Mrs. (singer), 177

Scott, Sir Walter, 144, 153, 158, 167, 185, 186

Sea Fight, The, 48

Second Part of Miscellany Poems, The, 166, 167, 187

Secret Love, 9, 143

Secular Masque, The, vii, xi, 123, 137, 184

Sedley, Sir Charles, viii

Select Collection of Modern Poems, A, 183

Seventeenth Century Lyrics, 168

Shadwell, Thomas, 145, 146

"Sharp was the Air, and cold was the Ground," 150

Silvia, 181

Sir Martin Mar-all, 9–11, 143, 144

Slade, Mrs. (singer), 155

Smith, D. Nichol, 160

Smith, John Stafford, 151

Smith, Robert, ix, 39, 41, 45, 47, 155–157

"So closely, closely prest In his *Clymena's* Arms young *Damon* lay," 156

Song for a Girl, 110

Song for St. Cecilia's Day, A, vii, xi, 75, 172

Song of a Scholar and his Mistress, 121

Song of Jealousie, 108

Song to a Fair, Young Lady, Going out of Town In the Spring, 101

Song to Apollo, 50, 158

Songs in Amphitryon, with the Musick, The, 139, 169–171

Songs in the Indian Queen, The, 141

Spanish Fryar, The, 58–60, 159, 160

Sprague, A. C., 169, 184

Squire, W. Barclay, 141, 142, 145, 146, 158, 166, 176

Staggins, Nicholas, ix, 37, 43, 151, 156

State of Innocence, The, 50, 157

Strunk, W., 160

Swinburne, A. C., 160

Sylvae: or, The Second Part of Poetical Miscellanies, 72–75, 166, 167

Taylor, Edward, 172

Tears of Amynta, for the Death of Damon, The, 64

Tea-Table Miscellany, The, 155, 162, 171, 186

Tempest, The, x, 11–17, 145–147

Ten Seventeenth Century Songs, 151

Theater of Music, The, 74, 166

Theatre of Ingenuity, The, 181

Thesaurus Musicus, 109, 171, 175, 176, 180, 181

Thorn-Drury, G., 154

"Thy sword within the scabbard keep," 185

Times Literary Supplement, The, 169

Town and Country Song-Book, The, 185

Troilus and Cressida, 54, 158

Turner (singer), 167

Tyndall, J., 143

Tyrannick Love, x, 17–22, 147, 148

Unfeigned Friendship, 159

Universal Harmony, 162, 177

Universal Magazine, The, 166

Unterricht von der teutschen Sprache und Poesie, 168, 183

V., R., Gent., 152

Veni Creator Spiritus, xi, 102, 179

Venice Preserved, viii

Vernon, Mrs. (singer), 185

Village Opera, The, 8, 143, 155

Vocal Enchantress, The, 177

Vocal Magazine, The, 180

Vocal Miscellany, The, 141, 148, 149, 160, 162, 167, 169, 171, 177, 179, 180

Vogel, Jakob, 167, 183

Voiture, Vincent, 144

Walpole, A. S., 179

Warton, Joseph, 162

Waters, Thomas, 160

Westminster-Drollery, 139, 143, 150–152

Westminster Drollery, the Second Part, 156

"We've cheated the parson," 177

"What shall I do to show how much I love her?" x

"Wherever I am and whatever I do," ix

William III, 163

Williams (singer), 167

Windsor-Drollery, 139, 143, 147–152

Wit and Drollery. Jovial Poems, 160

Wit and Mirth: or Pills to Purge Melancholy, 149–151, 160, 166, 168–170, 172, 173, 176–178, 180, 181

"With horns and with hounds," 185

Wits Academy, The, 143, 151, 156
Wits Cabinet, 161
Wit's Cabinet, 166, 169, 181
Woodson (singer), 167
Works of Henry Purcell, The, xi, 141, 142, 147, 148, 158, 166, 169–172, 176, 178

Works of John Dryden, The, 144, 154, 158, 167, 168, 185, 186
Wreath, The, 185
Wycherley, William, viii

Young-Mans Lamentation, The, 170

Mickey Mysteries
MYSTERY IN MIDAIR

Disney
PRESS

New York

Copyright © 2001 by Disney Enterprises, Inc.
All rights reserved. No part of this book may be reproduced or
transmitted in any form or by any means, electronic or mechanical, including
photocopying, recording, or by any information storage and retrieval system,
without written permission from the publisher. For information address
Disney Press, 114 Fifth Avenue, New York, New York 10011-5690.

Printed in the United States of America

First Edition
1 3 5 7 9 10 8 6 4 2

Library of Congress Catalog Card Number: 00-109810
ISBN 0-7868-4449-3

For more Disney Press fun, visit www.disneybooks.com

Chapter 1

PRECIOUS CARGO

On board Flight 815 to Center City, an elderly woman smiled and signaled to the flight attendant, who was coming down the aisle with her cart. "Miss, may I get a cup of herbal tea, please?" she asked.

The flight attendant nodded, then turned to the gentleman seated in the window seat next to the woman. "Would you like something to drink as well?" she asked.

"No, I would just like a little bit of peace!" he snapped, raising his voice and clutching the carry-on bag that he held in his lap.

Clearly surprised by his reaction, the flight attendant shrugged her shoulders, delivered the tea to the woman, and continued on down the aisle. Little did she know that the obviously nervous man was a famous jeweler by the name of Ernest Bauble. And the bag that he held in his lap contained some very important and very valuable cargo.

"Now, now . . . calm yourself," the elderly woman said to her neighbor. "A nice cup of herbal tea would do you some good."

But Mr. Bauble just turned away from her, gazed out the window, and threw his reply over his shoulder. "Herbal tea?" he scoffed. "But I might fall asleep! I can't let my guard down for a second."

"Now, why would you say a thing like that?" the woman responded. "The stuffy air on this plane is making you jumpy . . . and look, you're so pale. Are you sure you don't want some chamomile tea or warm milk to help you relax?"

Mr. Bauble did not answer, but glanced sideways at his neighbor. The jeweler was already imagining the most terrible things

about her motives. No doubt she's interested in the gems I'm carrying, he thought as he stared out the window again. Who knows what kind of tranquilizer she has ready to slip into my tea? Who knows if she's a little old woman at all? I've seen better disguises in movies!

A few minutes later, taking advantage of the fact that the woman had closed her eyes to rest, Mr. Bauble brought his hand up and yanked at her hair.

"Ouch!" she cried, rubbing her head and nearly jumping out of her seat. "What are you doing?"

The jeweler blushed and smilingly begged her pardon. Maybe I am letting my imagination run away with me, he thought.

Just then, a large man appeared from out of nowhere and loomed over them in the aisle. Okay, I'm finished, thought Mr. Bauble, his heart pounding in his chest. The jeweler seemed ready to crawl right inside his own coat and never come out again.

"Excuse me," the man said politely to Mr. Bauble. "Would you mind if my son looked

out your window? He'd like to look at the clouds, but our seats are in the center section." Only then did Mr. Bauble notice the man was holding a small child.

The jeweler did not say a word, assuming that this was some kind of setup. But the elderly woman responded for him.

"That would be fine," she said, reaching out to take the boy in her arms. "Come here, sweetie pie." Then, without a moment's hesitation, she turned and plunked the little boy right down onto Mr. Bauble's lap.

What next? thought Mr. Bauble, fuming.

With the little boy on his lap, the jeweler tried to relax. After all, he was a cute little devil. But Mr. Bauble just couldn't stop thinking about the contents of his bag.

I have to calm down, he thought. It feels as though everyone knows about these jewels. But no one even knows that I'm on this plane—except for the police. My wife would be worried sick if she knew that I was transporting millions of dollars' worth of precious gems.

An hour later, the flight attendant's voice came over the loudspeaker: "Ladies and gentlemen, we have begun our descent into Center City. Please put your seat backs and tray tables into their original upright positions and fasten your seat belts. . . ."

All the passengers followed the flight attendant's instructions—except for the jeweler, who refused to fasten his seat belt. He wouldn't take his hands off his bag for an instant.

"Oh, come, now," said the elderly woman kindly, trying to reassure him. "I was nervous about landing the first few times I flew, too. But everything will be just fine." As she spoke, she took the two ends of his seat belt and closed it snugly around him.

"Well!" the jeweler exclaimed, shocked by the woman's forward behavior.

"Oh, I'm sorry," the woman responded. "It's just that I can't wait for this plane to land. I'm going to visit my niece, Minnie. I haven't seen her in years. . . ."

Meanwhile, up in the cockpit, the captain prepared to lower the landing gear. "Flight eight-fifteen to control tower . . . eight-fifteen to control tower," he said.

"Control tower to Flight eight-fifteen," responded the controller. "Begin landing maneuver, runway number two."

"Hi, Robert," responded the pilot, recognizing his friend's voice. "We will be landing on runway two in approximately fifteen minutes."

"Yeah, as long as you can remember how

to land a plane!" Robert joked from the control tower.

Minutes later, Robert would wish that he could take his joke back.

Chapter 2

RADIO SILENCE

Ah, Sundays, thought Mickey. What a pleasure it was to stretch out on the couch with a thrilling mystery novel and a nice hot cup of tea.

It had been a very busy week at the detective agency that Mickey and Minnie ran together in Center City, and the two of them had been working around the clock to solve several urgent cases. In fact, the day before, Minnie had been called away to Software Valley to continue one of her investigations. She was scheduled to fly back to town that afternoon. In the meantime, Mickey was enjoying his quiet Sunday morning.

But, like all good things, his peace and quiet didn't last long. As the telephone rang, Detective Mickey sighed, put down his mystery novel and his tea, and crossed the room to the phone.

"Why, hello, Mickey! Did I wake you?"

It was Minnie! Mickey was so happy to hear her voice that his disappointment at the interruption immediately melted away.

"Hey, there, partner," said Mickey. "I wasn't sleeping, just trying to relax a little. What's going on? Did you finish your investigation?"

"Well," answered Minnie with a sigh, "I thought I would close the case of the stolen computer programs this morning. But unfortunately, it's more complicated than I thought. It looks like I have to stay in Software Valley at least until tonight."

"Gosh! Need any help?" Mickey offered.

"Aren't you sweet. I think I have everything under control *here*. But, you know, there *is* something you could do for me," said Minnie. "It doesn't have anything to do with work, though."

Always the gentleman, Mickey said, "I'd be more than happy to do anything I can."

"I was hoping you would say that," Minnie began, "because I was wondering if you could pick up my aunt Rita at the airport today. I had planned to meet her myself, but, as I said, I have to stay here a while longer."

"Your aunt Rita?" said Mickey excitedly. "She's coming to see you?"

"Yes, it's been at least three or four years since I've seen her, and I invited her to visit for a few days. But she's getting on in years, you know, and I'm afraid she wouldn't be able to find her way from the airport to my house on her own."

"Well, don't you worry about a thing," Mickey assured her. "So, what time does her plane land?"

"Uh, well . . . in about fifteen minutes. . . ."

The detective nearly dropped the phone as he jumped to his feet. He had to go!

"Oh, Mickey, thank you," Minnie continued. "I always said you were an angel! Aunt Rita is on AeroLine Flight eight-fifteen. And would you tell her I say hello and that I will be home as soon as I can? Bye-bye!"

Before Mickey even had time to respond, Minnie had hung up the phone. The detective glanced over at the novel on the couch, open to the second-to-last page, and sighed. He would have to find out whodunit later, because he certainly couldn't keep Minnie's sweet aunt Rita waiting!

Minutes later, as he hurried out of the house, Mickey nearly ran right into police inspector Burns, who was coming up the walkway to Mickey's front door.

"Hi, Inspector!" called Detective Mickey.

"Ah, Mickey," said Inspector Burns with a gasp. "Just the person I wanted to see. Do you have a moment?"

"Actually . . . I'm afraid I can't talk right now. I'm hurrying off to the airport—"

"What a coincidence!" interrupted Burns. "I was just coming to ask you to come with *me* to the airport."

"Going away, Inspector?" asked Mickey. "Finally taking that vacation?"

"Oh, I wish that were the case," said Burns with a sigh. "But I'm afraid I'm here on business. Something terrible has happened. About ten minutes ago, AeroLine Flight eight-fifteen disappeared."

Mickey was speechless. That was Aunt Rita's flight! He turned to Inspector Burns. "But—but how is that possible? Tell me what happened. . . ."

The inspector shook his head. "At the moment, I don't know anything more than you do. As soon as I got the call from the airport, I came over to get you. I have a feeling that I'm going to need all the help I can get on this investigation. Will you come with me? We have to get to the airport as quickly as possible."

Together, they hopped into the inspector's car and took off at top speed, sirens blaring.

At the airport, Mickey and Inspector Burns found a horrible scene. Dozens of people were crowding the AeroLine ticket counter, desperate for information about the plane carrying their family and friends.

"But the flight wasn't supposed to be late!" cried a young man.

"My husband and son are on board that

flight," shouted a woman with tears in her eyes. "Tell me what is happening or I will call the police!" Mickey could read the anger and anxiety on all of their faces.

Somehow, Mickey and Inspector Burns managed to get through the crowd to the security checkpoint, where some agents were waiting to accompany them to the control tower.

Inside the control tower, the scene was just as tense. Air-traffic controllers and investigators were pacing back and forth; others were examining the flight plan of AeroLine 815 for the hundredth time; still others were staring out into the sky through the large windows.

"I don't understand this at all!" exclaimed Robert, the chief air-traffic controller, as he recounted his story to Burns. "Everything was going by the book. Then, all of a sudden—*poof!*—the plane was gone!"

"Let's start from the beginning," responded the inspector. "At what time did you lose contact with the plane?"

"Fourteen minutes before its scheduled

landing, it completely disappeared from my radar screen and radio communication was interrupted," said Robert. "Only a minute or so before that, I was joking with the pilot."

"Is it possible that the plane is simply lost?" asked the inspector.

"Well, there *was* heavy cloud cover," responded Robert, "but the visibility was acceptable and pilots are trained to fly in worse conditions. And, in case of any difficulty, pilots can always use the S.L.S."

"I'm sorry," interrupted the investigator. "What is S.L.S.?"

"The Safe-Landing System," Robert explained. "It's an advanced capability that allows the plane to make an entirely automatic landing. And besides, until it disappeared from the radar, Flight eight-fifteen was right on target, following the correct route."

At the inspector's side, with notebook in hand, Detective Mickey was taking down the important points. Then he scratched his head thoughtfully and posed a question. "Were there any other planes scheduled to land at the same time as Flight eight-fifteen?"

"Not at the exact same time. But in the fifteen minutes after eight-fifteen was scheduled to land, three other flights landed without a problem."

Inspector Burns raised an eyebrow. "Is it possible that the pilot decided to delay his landing due to air traffic?"

"Absolutely impossible!" exclaimed Robert. "A pilot can't make decisions like that. He must follow the instructions from the tower.

When there is heavy traffic, planes are sometimes instructed to move away to a safer area of the sky, then circle until they are given permission to land. But Flight eight-fifteen was right on schedule, and it had the right of way. I just can't imagine what's happened to the plane! We even called other local airports, but no one has any information at all."

Minutes later, Detective Mickey and Inspector Burns finished their questioning, thanked Robert and his coworkers, and left the control tower.

"So now what, Inspector?" Mickey asked.

"Well," responded Burns sorrowfully, "I'm afraid that at this point we have to begin the search for the crash site."

Detective Mickey nodded sadly. He thought of all of the passengers, and of one in particular. He couldn't bear to think how upset Minnie would be when she heard the news.

Chapter 3

THE SEARCH FOR
FLIGHT 815

Police officers, firefighters, security officers
. . . they were all working furiously to locate
the wreckage of Flight 815.

The search was not easy. The airport was
surrounded by densely wooded mountains
on all sides. But many of the locals showed
up to give a hand in the search, and their help
was invaluable, since they knew the area better than anyone else.

As for Detective Mickey and Inspector
Burns, they combed the surrounding area
from the sky in a police helicopter.

"From up here it will be easier to spot anything out of the ordinary!" the Inspector shouted over the loud roar of the helicopter's blades.

Detective Mickey kept his eyes peeled on the ground through the binoculars he wore around his neck. Soon he could make out the various search parties. Some were scouring the mountains on foot; others drove along the dirt roads in all-terrain vehicles. The heads of each search party were in constant radio contact with the inspector.

After a couple of hours, the helicopter pilot was preparing to fly over the search area a third time. So far, they hadn't seen a thing. No news had come in over the radio. In the helicopter, there was a heavy silence. Then, suddenly . . .

"Look!" shouted Detective Mickey, sitting up in his seat. "Down there on the right: it looks like part of the fuselage of an airplane!"

The helicopter pilot tried to fly in for a closer look.

"It's too dangerous," warned the pilot. "The forest is too dense here—there's not enough room to land."

Burns immediately made contact with the search party closest to the site so that they could investigate.

"Impossible, Inspector," an agent responded from the ground. "The rain over the last few days has made the ground very slippery, and we can't get over there. We'll have to call in some mountaineers, or else take the path on the other side of the mountain."

"There's not enough time," Mickey insisted. "In two hours it will be dark. If there are any survivors, we have to get to them immediately. I see only one solution," he concluded firmly, taking hold of a rope ladder lying in the back of the helicopter cabin.

"Mickey, are you crazy? It's too risky!" Burns exclaimed anxiously.

But Detective Mickey was practically out the door already. And he wasn't going to be talked out of it.

"I'll get as close as I can," the pilot assured him. "Good luck!"

Mickey secured one end of the rope ladder to the inside of the helicopter and let the other end fall down into the open air. Then, after taking a deep breath, he began to climb down the rungs of the ladder. All of a sudden, a strong gust of wind made him lose his balance. Taken off guard, Mickey was losing his grip on the ladder!

Burns looked on from above, holding his breath. His friend was about to fall to his death! Luckily, though, at the last second, Mickey's foot got caught in the last rung of the ladder. He dangled upside down in midair.

Just then, the pilot noticed his fuel gauge. "We're running out of fuel!" he shouted to the inspector. "We have five more minutes, but then we'll have no choice but to start back to the base."

Meanwhile, Detective Mickey was trying to reach the ladder with his hands so he could pull himself up.

"Stay calm!" Burns shouted to Mickey, after giving instructions to the pilot. "We're going to try to get close to a tree so you have something to grab on to. When you're safe, we'll release the ladder."

With his head and arms dangling, Mickey tried to catch hold of a branch of the nearest

pine tree. Twice, he tried and failed, and then . . . got it!

Burns cheered and, as soon as the inspector had unhooked the ladder, the helicopter flew off to the base to refuel.

Meanwhile, Mickey managed to untangle his foot from the rope and begin climbing down the tree, trying not to look down. He had ended up in the highest branches of one of the tallest trees around—he was at least a hundred feet off the ground.

To make matters worse, he was being pricked by a thousand spiny needles. Aw, gee, did I have to end up in a pine tree? thought Mickey.

And as if that wasn't enough, the wind continued to blow in strong gusts. The treetop swayed from side to side, so much so that Mickey was getting seasick. But finally, Mickey managed to climb down to a lower branch that hung six feet from the ground, above a nice fluffy pile of dry leaves. One big jump and the detective found himself back on the ground, safe and sound.

Immediately, Mickey took off toward the

pieces of metal he had seen from the air. There he discovered what he had thought was wreckage—an old rusty trunk, a few tires, and two old car doors. It was the remains of an abandoned automobile.

"Mickey . . . do you copy? Mickey, do you read me? Come in. . . ."

It was Burns's voice, coming over the walkie-talkie. Detective Mickey took the radio from his belt.

"I read you loud and clear," said Mickey.

"I'm fine . . . but I didn't find what we were looking for."

"Not to worry . . . I'm sending the helicopter back to pick you up."

A few hours later, the heads of all of the search parties met at police headquarters.

"There's no trace of the plane," declared the fire chief.

"Residents of the surrounding area have been questioned," the police chief interjected, "but nobody saw or heard anything. And one thing's for sure: if a plane of that size crashes to the ground, you can hear it for miles around!"

It was incredible. Everyone was basically saying that Flight 815 had disappeared into thin air!

Detective Mickey was still at police headquarters when his cell phone rang. It was Minnie. She was in tears.

"Oh, Mickey, I can't believe it!" she exclaimed. "I heard the news—there was a special report on TV. Please . . . tell me what happened!"

"Well," Mickey began gently, "it seems that

the plane has disappeared. But it's a strange case—too complicated to explain over the phone. Do you want me to fly out and meet you in Software Valley?"

"No, I've already booked a flight home tonight. I've finished my investigation of the software thefts. I'll E-mail you my report, and then I'm leaving for the airport."

"Okay, Minnie . . . I'll be waiting for you. Try to get some rest on the flight."

Chapter 4

MINNIE, COME HOME!

It was 11 P.M. Most of the police and investigators had gone home after a long day's work. But Inspector Burns and Detective Mickey were still at police headquarters, hoping for news of the missing plane.

"It couldn't have vanished without a trace!" Mickey exclaimed, pacing nervously.

"Please, Mickey, stop. You're giving me a headache," said the inspector. He sighed and looked shrewdly into Mickey's eyes. "Look, maybe it's time I filled you in. . . ."

The detective turned to Burns with a look of surprise on his face, then sat down in front of him and asked, "What do you mean? Have you been keeping something from me?"

"Well ... on Flight eight-fifteen," the inspector began, "there was a certain passenger ... by the name of Ernest Bauble, a jeweler transporting precious stones worth several million dollars—"

"Millions?!" Mickey nearly fell off his chair. "But why didn't you tell me?"

"I'm sorry, Mickey. We had to keep that information secret. But, given the circumstances ..."

"So there *could* be another explanation. The plane could have been hijacked. It could have taken another route," Mickey hypothesized.

Burns rubbed at his temples, thinking hard. "But, if that were the case, the radar would have shown the change in course. It just doesn't add up."

Mickey's eyes met the inspector's for a moment, and the inspector quickly looked away.

"I get the feeling you're still holding something back," said Mickey.

Burns got up from his chair, then sat back down, then stood up again. He was obviously nervous. Finally, he turned and said, "Mickey, try to understand . . . there are certain things I am not authorized to reveal. . . ."

"I realize that. But, don't you see, Inspector? You're wasting our time. If you want me to be helpful in this investigation, I need to know everything!"

"All right, all right," said Burns with a sigh, loosening his tie. "I'll tell you. This week, there were three scheduled shipments of gems to be delivered to our city. So as not to attract attention, the proprietor of the jewels, Mr. Bauble, decided to use normal commercial airlines, although of course, he notified the police. Flight eight-fifteen was the first of the three flights with the shipments."

Mickey listened carefully as he sipped his tea, then asked, "When is the second shipment scheduled to depart?"

"In just over a half an hour," Burns replied. "It's AeroLine Flight six-thirty from Software Valley."

Detective Mickey stared in surprise.

"Oh, no! Minnie!" he cried. Then, turning to the inspector, he shouted, "Call it off! We have to stop that flight from taking off!"

"Impossible," responded Burns. "For security reasons, we just can't do that. I'm sorry, but there's really nothing I can do. But I'm sure everything will be fine. There's no reason to think that this flight will disappear, too."

But Mickey could not calm down, no matter how hard he tried. He pulled out his cell phone and furiously punched in Minnie's number. A recorded, metallic-sounding voice responded, telling him that his partner was unreachable.

Mickey groaned. "She probably forgot to charge her battery. She had a million other things on her mind."

The detective did not give up easily, though. Next, he dialed the number of her hotel in Software Valley.

"I'm sorry," responded the concierge, "but she has already left. She took a taxi to the airport about half an hour ago."

"By any chance, do you know what flight she was taking?" asked Mickey, his heart in his throat.

"Actually, I made the reservation for her myself. Just a moment, let me get my notes."

Mickey was getting more and more nervous every second.

"Hello? Here it is," said the concierge. "The reservation was for AeroLine Flight six-thirty, leaving from Software Valley in about half an hour. Does that help?"

Mickey was barely able to bring himself to thank the concierge before he hung up. He put the phone down slowly. Minnie was in terrible danger, and there was nothing he could do to help her!

Miles away, Minnie's taxi had come to a dead stop in a huge traffic jam in downtown Software Valley. In the backseat, Minnie kept checking her watch and craning her neck to see out the front window.

"Please, sir," Minnie begged the taxi driver, "you've got to do something. My flight leaves in a few minutes."

"Oh, no problem, miss," the driver replied sarcastically. "I'll just push this magic button here on the dashboard, and the taxi will sprout wings and fly over the top of all the other cars." He smirked at her in the rearview

mirror. But, then, as he noticed the troubled look on Minnie's face, he softened up a little. "Don't worry. I'll get you there on time."

If Minnie had only known that the traffic was a blessing in disguise. . . .

About an hour later, Mickey and Inspector Burns were back at the airport.

"Let's get a move on," said Mickey, pointing the inspector toward the escalator that led to the control tower.

Inside the tower, huge radar screens illuminated the room with their greenish glow. Several air-traffic controllers were busy communicating with pilots of incoming airplanes.

Mickey and Burns stood behind the controller who was following the progress of Flight 630. At any moment, the flight was due to appear on the radar screens . . . or at least that's what Mickey was hoping as he thought about his friend on board.

Suddenly the controller announced: "There it is! We've made contact with Flight six-thirty."

The plane had just become visible as a little yellow triangle on the outer edge of the radar screen. Everything seemed to be going smoothly: the plane was following the correct route and there was very little other air traffic at that time of night.

A few minutes later, the pilot's voice crackled over the radio:

"Six-thirty to control tower . . ."

"Control tower to six-thirty . . ." responded the controller. "You're cleared to land on

runway one, over."

"Roger, initiating landing procedure . . ." came the pilot's reply.

Mickey breathed a sigh of relief. He had been so worried for Minnie, but it seemed that everything would be fine, after all.

"Six-thirty, please confirm runway number," said the controller. "You are cleared to land on runway number one."

This time, there was no response.

"Control tower to six-thirty, over," the controller called again.

Static crackled over the radio for a few seconds, and then . . . there was complete silence.

At the exact same moment, the little yellow triangle completely vanished from the radar screen.

The airplane was gone.

"Minnie!" screamed Mickey.

Chapter 5

TWO MISSING PLANES

In a panic, Mickey ran over to the large windows of the control tower, but he couldn't see a thing in the black sky above the airport.

Robert, the chief air-traffic controller, sat completely dazed at the control panel. "I've been doing this for fifteen years," he mumbled, "and I never seen anything like this. Two planes that disappear into thin air within hours of each other, and for no apparent reason."

"And there was no distress call, no SOS!" replied Detective Mickey. "It doesn't make sense! And how is it possible that the aircraft disappeared from the radar?"

"I have no idea," responded the controller. "It's possible for the cockpit instruments that allow us to track the plane to malfunction. But it's hard to believe that the same thing could happen to two planes on the same day—"

"Robert," Burns interrupted, stepping up to the control panel, "can you pinpoint the plane's exact location when we lost the signal?"

The controller unfolded a map of the region and pointed to the coast.

"I'll alert the Coast Guard immediately," declared the inspector, picking up the telephone and dialing the emergency number. After he had hung up, he turned to Detective Mickey. "I don't think there's any sense in us going out there, Mickey. I have asked that all findings be reported immediately to police headquarters."

"Well," said Mickey, his shoulders drooping with grief, "let's go, then."

It was three in the morning before a fax

finally arrived at headquarters with some news.

"It's a report from the Coast Guard," said the inspector as he pulled out the fax. He read it aloud:

"'We have surveyed the area of the disappearance for over two hours without finding a trace of the plane. Several search parties have questioned the lighthouse keeper and residents of the surrounding area, with no results. We cannot locate any witnesses who saw or heard an explosion. The search will continue again at first light. Signed: Captain W. Mann.'"

"I can't believe it!" Detective Mickey exclaimed. "There is something very strange going on here. Something . . . or someone . . . is making these planes disappear. And I am going to figure it out."

"Mickey," said the inspector, putting a hand on his shoulder, "maybe we should both get some rest. Go home and try to sleep—you need it. The Coast Guard can't do anything else until tomorrow morning. We'll take stock of the situation again then."

• • •

Meanwhile, in a clearing in the woods, not far from the city, about a dozen masked men dressed all in black were unloading crates from the cargo hold of an airplane. Nearby, an enormous black tarp hid another plane, leaving only the nose exposed.

"We've unloaded the crates of gold from the second plane," said a voice from under one of the dark masks. "But there's no trace of precious stones on the first plane. Maybe we got a bad tip. . . ."

"Keep looking!" responded a loud, gruff voice. "I'm going to check on the passengers."

"Okay, boss."

Inside a cold stone building nearby, the passengers of Flights 815 and 630 stood huddled together, waiting to find out what the masked men planned to do with them.

"What is going on here?" whispered the pilot of Flight 815 to the pilot of Flight 630. "I was sure I landed at the right airport. I spoke with Robert, the air-traffic controller, and I followed his instructions to the letter."

The other pilot nodded. "The same thing happened to me. I just don't understand how we ended up here."

The pilots quickly grew silent when they saw one of their captors enter the room.

"Okay, ladies and gentlemen, now do me the favor of emptying your purses and pockets onto that table over there," he ordered. "Otherwise I will have no choice but to search each and every one of you!"

"Well, I never!" replied Minnie's aunt Rita. "What kind of manners are these? Who do you think you are, young man?"

Mr. Bauble, who was standing against the wall next to her, leaned over and whispered, "Be quiet, I'm telling you. Don't attract their attention."

"I don't care," the spunky woman shot back. "This is no way to treat people!" Aunt Rita turned to face the ringleader. "Not only have you rerouted our flight without permission, but now you want to rob us? Well, if you dare touch my purse, you'll regret it!" Then she brandished her purse at the man as if it were a weapon.

The man burst out laughing and approached Aunt Rita. But as he reached out to grab the purse, she grabbed him roughly by the arm, yanked it around, and pinned his arm behind his back. He cried out in pain.

"Not so funny now, is it?" said Aunt Rita, still twisting his arm.

The scream of their leader brought the other hijackers running into the room. But

the moment they saw what was going on, they stopped in their tracks and doubled over with laughter.

"Don't just stand there!" the ringleader yelled angrily. "Do something!"

"Okay, ma'am . . . now just let him go!" said one of the masked men as he turned to Aunt Rita.

The man was armed, so Aunt Rita had no choice but to obey. She let go of the ringleader's arm and stepped away.

Finally free, the head bandit complained in a high whining voice. "Owww . . . that woman could have broken my arm!" Then, in a sterner tone, he ordered, "Get back to work, all of you! We've lost enough time as it is! Find those gems in the cargo hold, or none of you will see a single ounce of the gold we've found."

The masked men obeyed and filed out of the room, with their boss following behind them. When they were gone, the passengers gathered around Aunt Rita, patting her on the back.

"Way to go!" said one man.

"Now maybe they'll leave us alone for a while," said another.

"Where did you learn that move?" a young woman asked.

Aunt Rita smiled. Then she leaned forward and gestured for her fellow passengers to lean in close. "Well," she said, "I'll let you all in on a little secret. I hate crosswords, I don't know how to knit, and television puts me to sleep. I had to find something to amuse myself, so I took a self-defense class at the Martial Arts Center. I don't mean to brag," said Aunt Rita coyly, "but I'm the best in my group!"

There was no doubt about it: Aunt Rita was naturally brave, and anyone who knew the family realized that her niece, Minnie, had inherited her courage.

But speaking of Minnie, where was she? Why wasn't she there, among the passengers of Flight 630 from Software Valley?

Chapter 6

WELCOME HOME!

Following Burns's advice, Mickey was heading home. He was very tired, but his mind just couldn't stop going over and over the facts. Two airplanes couldn't just disappear without a trace!

Then, as he passed Minnie's house, Mickey looked up and saw the light on in the living room. Hmm ... thought Mickey. Had someone broken into Minnie's house? He had to check it out. Mickey crept up the walkway to the house and tried the door. It wasn't locked. Slowly and silently, Mickey pushed the door open, stepped inside, and ...

"Why, hello, Mickey."

Seated in a comfy armchair, Minnie was sipping a cup of tea.

"Min . . . Min . . ." stammered her partner, shocked beyond belief.

"Minnie. My name is Minnie. Don't you remember me?" she teased. Then her smile faded and she became serious. "Is there any news about my aunt Rita?"

But Mickey was still trying to figure out how Minnie had gotten home. He was trying to solve the puzzle of Flight 630.

"So your flight didn't disappear, and it didn't explode," he thought aloud, "and it didn't fall into the ocean. . . ." As he spoke, Mickey picked up the phone and began to dial the inspector's number.

"What are you talking about?" said Minnie. "What plane? And who are you calling at this hour?"

"I have to tell Burns."

Calmly, Detective Minnie got up from her chair and walked over to Mickey. She took the phone from his hands and placed it back in the cradle.

"Mickey, I came home on the train."

"What?"

Minnie shrugged. "I got stuck in a traffic jam and I missed my flight," she explained. "So I got myself down to the Software Valley train station and managed to catch an express."

Mickey reached out and hugged his friend. He was so relieved that she was safe. Then he began filling her in on all the details pertaining to the case. Minnie wanted to know everything.

A half hour later, Mickey sat back and said, "There, now you know as much as I do."

"Another aircraft investigation," Detective Minnie commented. "I'll be an expert."

Mickey's brow wrinkled. "Another?" he asked. "I don't remember having a case like this before."

"Actually," said Minnie, "I was talking about my investigation in Software Valley. I collected some evidence related to the disappearance of an airport computer program—a program used in control towers...." Minnie trailed off and sat up. "Wait a minute! Could the two cases be related?"

Mickey stared at his friend, perplexed. "What are you thinking?"

Minnie thought it over for a minute. "I'm not sure. Let me sleep on it," she said at last. "It's late and I'm very tired and preoccupied. But for now, let's just be clear about the facts: we're almost positive that the planes didn't crash, because the search parties didn't turn up anything. So they must have been rerouted, but to where? And how and by whom?"

Mickey, unfortunately, didn't have any answers.

"Assuming that there *are* hijackers involved," Minnie continued, "it's possible that one of the air-traffic controllers is working with them."

Detective Mickey shook his head. "Burns told me he conducted a very discreet investigation, and all the controllers checked out fine. They had no knowledge of the valuable cargo on board the two planes."

Minnie was quiet for a few minutes. When she spoke again, her eyes were filled with tears. "When I think of poor Aunt Rita . . ." she murmured. "Who knows where she is right now. . . ."

"I'm sure she's fine, Minnie. The hijackers must be interested in the jewels, not the passengers. We'll find her. But right now, I think we just need to get some sleep. Good night."

Minnie yawned. "Good night, Mickey."

Early the next morning, Minnie was awakened by a knock at the door.

"It's Mickey!"

"It's open," she responded sleepily.

Detective Mickey came inside and found his partner wrapped up in a blanket on the sofa. Wow, thought Mickey, she really was tired last night!

"I've got an idea!" exclaimed Mickey.

Minnie stretched and sat up. "What is it?"

"Get ready and follow me."

"Where?"

"To police headquarters," Mickey said urgently. "We don't have any time to lose."

Detective Minnie would have loved a few more hours of sleep, but she knew that when Mickey was on a roll, it was useless to try to stop him.

Burns was reading through some documents when he saw Minnie come through the door.

"Min . . . Min . . ." babbled the inspector, staring at Minnie.

"You sound just like Mickey!" Detective Minnie joked.

Mickey chuckled for a moment, but then he quickly turned serious. "Inspector, when is the plane with the third jewel shipment scheduled to take off?"

"This afternoon at three, from San Rico."

"Which flight is it?"

"AeroLine Flight five-ten."

Mickey looked at his watch and made some quick calculations. "San Rico is about five hours from here by car. If we leave soon, we can make it there before the plane takes off."

Minnie held up her hand. "Excuse me, but can you tell us what it is we're going to do when we get there?" she asked.

"Well, Minnie," said Mickey with a wink, "have you ever wondered what it would be like to be a flight attendant?"

Minnie eyed her partner suspiciously. "What exactly do you mean?"

"Yes, please explain," added Burns.

"It's very simple," said Mickey, flopping into a chair. "Minnie will go on board Flight five-ten posing as a flight attendant. Then, after the plane has taken off, she can enter the cockpit without arousing any suspicion. That way she'll be able to observe the flight from the inside." Mickey paused. "There's just one small obstacle, Inspector."

"And what's that?"

"Well . . . we would need to replace one of the airline's regular flight attendants. But, given your good relationship with the police of San Rico," concluded Detective Mickey, "maybe you could . . . arrange something?"

"Fine with me," responded Burns with a shrug. "Minnie, what do you think?"

"It sounds a little risky . . ." Minnie began. "But I think I can handle it!"

"Meanwhile, I'll go up in a fighter plane," Mickey continued. "Inspector, would you ask the San Rico police to have one ready for me. . . ."

"A fighter plane!" shouted Inspector Burns, his eyes bulging out of his head. "Have you lost your mind?"

"Well . . ." said Mickey, "can you think of another way to follow an airplane? Besides, I have a license to fly military jets."

Burns sat back in his chair and rubbed his eyes. "All right, all right. I'll do it. But just . . ."

The inspector didn't get a chance to finish

his sentence. When he opened his eyes again, the two detectives were already out the door, heading off on a new and dangerous adventure.

Meanwhile, miles and miles away, a cell phone call was being made from inside an airplane hangar in San Rico.

"Hello, Weasel? It's Eagle. Can you hear me?"

"Loud and clear," answered a gruff voice. "Have you done it?"

"Of course," said Eagle. "This time it was a little more difficult to sabotage the navigational instruments. But don't worry. Our little bird will fly straight into the nest you've built," said the criminal, chuckling evilly.

"Good," Weasel replied. "I'll wait for you here at base and make sure you get your share."

Chapter 7

DIRECT FROM SAN RICO

With just a couple of telephone calls, Inspector Burns had set everything up. His colleague in the San Rico Police Department was happy to help and spoke immediately with the head of airport security. Everything was proceeding according to Detective Mickey's plan.

In her flight attendant uniform, Minnie welcomed the passengers aboard Flight 510 like a true pro. After she and the other flight attendants had presented the plane's safety features, the plane was ready for take-off.

Detective Minnie sneaked a peek at the radio transmitter hidden in the inside pocket of her jacket. Mickey had given it to her. It seemed to be working: the green light was on, meaning that she could communicate with her partner in the fighter plane at any time.

"May I have a glass of water?" asked a young woman.

"Of course," responded Minnie with a smile.

Then an elderly man was feeling chilly, so Minnie brought him a blanket.

Later, a woman rang her call button: "Excuse me, miss, but my daughter is not feeling well." The little girl was looking very pale.

"Hmm . . . she doesn't seem to have a fever," Minnie judged, placing her hand to the little girl's forehead. "Maybe it's just a touch of airsickness. I'll get something to help her feel better."

Mickey was settling into the cockpit of his fighter plane. He had always dreamed of flying, and he had really enjoyed Captain

Limburger's course, which he had taken to get his pilot's license.

"You never know," Mickey had said to Minnie at the time, "it could come in handy for one of our investigations." She hadn't been particularly enthusiastic about the idea. But, in the end, he had been right, and there he was, seated in front of the controls.

Everything was going as planned: Mickey followed behind the airliner at a safe distance, flying at a lower altitude and beneath the clouds so that he couldn't be seen. Below, he could make out the hills and forests that surrounded Center City. They were getting close to the airport!

Mickey relaxed when he heard the serene voice of the pilot through his headphones: his radio had been specially tuned so that he could hear all communications between the pilot of Flight 510 and the control tower. The airplane was not far from the runway now.

Burns stood in the airport control tower, watching the two planes—510 and Mickey's jet—on one of the radar screens.

Flight 510 was scheduled to land in fifteen minutes, but an overdue aircraft had just requested clearance to land on the same runway. As 510 began to circle in the air a few miles from the airport, waiting for the other plane to land, Detective Mickey looked down at his instrument panel and gasped. He was almost out of gas! Ugh! he thought. I should have known! His military jet had a much smaller gas tank than the larger passenger jet. Mickey had to land. He made one last check of 510's position. Then he prepared to land the fighter on one of the airport's smaller side runways.

As soon as his fighter jet touched down at the airport, Mickey jumped out and ran to the control tower. He took one look at the distressed faces of Robert and the inspector, and he knew that it had happened again.

"We've lost contact with Flight five-ten," Burns declared anxiously.

"What!" said Mickey in shock. "But I was following them until just a moment ago!"

"I don't know how it could have

happened," said Robert. "We were following five-ten and your plane on the radar screens. But as soon as you landed, the signal of the other plane disappeared, just like Flight eight-fifteen and Flight six-thirty."

Right away, Mickey thought of Minnie. "The radio transmitter!" he exclaimed. "I'll try to get in touch with Minnie." Then they would finally know the truth about the missing aircraft.

But all of his attempts to make contact with her failed. Detective Mickey was getting no answer.

Meanwhile, on board Flight 510, Minnie glanced suspiciously at her watch.

That's strange, she thought. We should've landed nine minutes ago.

Minnie ducked into the plane's tiny bathroom and tried to call Mickey using the radio transmitter, but she wasn't able to establish a connection. Then she spotted a flashing red light on the radio—a sign that something wasn't working.

Next, Minnie exited the bathroom and

worked her way up into the cockpit to see what was going on.

But to her surprise, the pilot and copilot were cool and calm. No hijackers or equipment problems to speak of.

"What a beautiful blue sky, up here above the clouds," the captain said to her, smiling. "I almost don't want to land. What do you think?"

"Yes, it really is a beautiful day to fly," she

responded mechanically, thinking that perhaps she was nervous for no reason. After all, it wasn't so strange for a plane to land a few minutes late.

Then, Minnie smiled and relaxed as she looked out the front windows of the cockpit and saw the runways and the hangars of the airport just ahead.

"Flight attendants, please prepare for landing," the pilot announced over the loudspeaker. "We have begun our descent."

The large, white plane descended smoothly onto the runway and, after coming to a stop, began taxiing toward its assigned arrival gate. It pulled up to the gate, and the doors of the plane were pushed open. The pilots stepped out of the cockpit and lined up by the exit, preparing to say good-bye to the passengers as they left the plane.

That's when a loud scream from one of the flight attendants startled everyone on board. Suddenly, several hooded men carrying weapons came out of nowhere and blocked the door of the plane.

"Leave your bags and purses on your seats

and get off the plane . . . NOW!" one of them ordered in a threatening voice.

Terrorized, the passengers and crew silently obeyed and filed out the door of the plane. Only the sound of a crying baby broke the silence.

Chapter 8
SOS

Hidden between two rows of airplane seats, Minnie tried not to make a sound.

"Boss, should we take the purses now?" she heard one of the hijackers ask. Detective Minnie's heart skipped a beat: if they began looking among the rows of seats, they'd find her within minutes. But thankfully . . .

"There's no time now," came the reply. "Right now we need to focus on the passengers and the cargo. We'll do the rest later."

Minnie breathed a huge sigh of relief. Seconds later, there was silence in the airplane cabin, and she could finally peek over the seat. Everyone was gone, but she knew she would have to be careful. Out one of the cabin windows, she saw the passengers moving away from the plane, escorted by a dozen of the masked men. Without losing a moment, she pulled out her radio transmitter. The green light was on!

"Hello! Mickey, it's Minnie . . . hello! Come in, Mickey . . . come in!"

From the control tower, Detective Mickey noticed clouds slowly moving in over the city. He glanced down at his belt: because of the weather, his radio transmitter wasn't receiving a signal. If Minnie tried to call, she could not reach him now.

"They must have landed. But where?" wondered Mickey. "More and more, this seems like something out of a science-fiction film!"

Suddenly, the green light flashed on Mickey's radio. Finally they had made contact.

"Mickey!" called Minnie's voice from Mickey's transmitter.

"Minnie!" he shouted happily. "Where are you?"

"We've been taken hostage," his partner whispered. "The hijackers are armed and dangerous. They are searching the plane for the gold and jewels. They seem very determined."

Minnie's voice got softer and softer—the radio signal was going in and out.

"Where are you?" shouted the detective, trying to zero in on the important details.

But Mickey could only make out a few words from his friend's response:

"Airport . . . program . . . agency . . ."

"Minnie! Minnie!" Mickey called. But it was too late: the signal was lost.

Looking out from the control tower, Mickey did not see anything out of the ordinary. The investigator didn't know what to think anymore. He knew that if his partner said "airport," it probably meant she was at an airport! But if the airplane had landed there at Center City, he would have seen it!

While Mickey tried to reason it out, Minnie tried contacting him again. But just then, a voice startled her from behind.

"Looking for something, miss?"

Minnie jumped and turned: a few feet away, two furious eyes were glaring down at her from under a black hood. It was the leader of the hijackers—she recognized the voice that had ordered everyone off the plane. She hadn't heard him sneak up on her.

"Who were you talking to?" he growled, as he came closer.

With faster hands than any magician, the detective managed to hide the radio transmitter in the pocket of her jacket before the hijacker could see it.

"Nobody," she replied in a trembling voice. "I always talk to myself when I'm afraid . . ."

Luckily, the hijacker seemed to buy her little story.

"Come on!" he shouted. He led her to the door of the plane. "Off with the others, NOW!" He pushed her toward the stairs and then called for one of his accomplices.

Minnie didn't protest: she understood that it was better to do what they said. And this way, maybe she could see what was going on. Besides, she still had her radio; she would try again to get in touch with Mickey.

Hmm . . . thought Minnie as she walked toward the other hostages. What fresh, clean air! I'd almost swear we're in the mountains, not at the airport.

Then she stopped, looked around, and listened: complete silence. Not a single sound of airplanes taking off or landing. Strange, since the air traffic was usually heavy at that time of day.

Prodded on by the hijacker, Minnie passed in front of the open entrance of a huge hangar. Inside, she could make out the outlines of two airplanes covered by huge tarps. Then, the scoundrel led her into a stone structure that looked like an old, abandoned house. Inside there were dozens and dozens of passengers—more than just the passengers on her flight—being watched by several armed men. Minnie scanned the crowd. She recognized several of the passengers from her flight. But who were all the others? Could these be the passengers from Flights 815 and 630?

"Aunt Rita!" shouted the detective, spotting her aunt in the crowd. She ran over to hug her. "I was really worried about you! I'm so happy to see you!"

"Minnie! What are you doing here?" Aunt Rita exclaimed.

"I'll explain later. Now tell me: how have they been treating you?"

Aunt Rita shrugged. "We're all fine. Just a bit hungry, that's all." Then the woman turned to the jeweler, who had just moved

the contents of his bag to the inside pocket of his coat. "Allow me to introduce my niece, Minnie," she said to him.

She was about to add something when she heard the sound of a baby crying. Aunt Rita and Minnie turned toward a woman seated on a big crate with a baby in her arms.

"My son is hungry," the anxious mother explained, "but his bottle is on the plane."

"Come on, let's be strong," said Aunt Rita, putting an arm around her. "I am sure the police are looking for us and that soon we will all be safe and sound. Right, Minnie?"

Let's hope so . . . thought the detective as she nodded to her aunt.

Chapter 9
ON THE TRAIL

Mickey and Inspector Burns were trying to fit the pieces together. From what Minnie had said over the radio, Mickey reasoned, it seemed that the passengers of the missing airplanes were being held hostage in some unknown airport.

The inspector, however, was not convinced. "How can that be? All of the airports in the area are under tight security. Three passenger airplanes and all of those people are not easy to hide. We would have found them by now."

"Yet, according to Minnie, she is at an

airport . . ." replied Mickey, who was turning his partner's words over and over in his mind.

Just then, Mickey overheard two control tower technicians talking about the Internet and computer software.

"Of course!" exclaimed Mickey, hitting his forehead with the palm of his hand. "Why didn't I think of it sooner?" Mickey rushed over and asked one of the technicians if he could use a computer to check his E-mail at the Mickey and Minnie Detective Agency.

"Programs, agency, airport: it all makes sense now!" said Mickey. "The investigation in Software Valley . . . that's what Minnie was talking about over the radio."

Then he turned to the inspector and explained. "On our drive to San Rico for the setup, Minnie told me about the theft of a computer software program in Software Valley. The program contained a database with a catalog of virtual images—images of every airport in the world."

A few moments later, he was reading his partner's report on-screen:

Investigative Report: Software Valley

Re: Theft of VIRTUAL AIRPORT Program

The program was stolen approximately two months ago from the aeronautic base in Software Valley. This program makes it possible to project a full-sized, realistic image of any airport in a specified physical location.

Each of these virtual images represents the actual airport in every detail. The precision of the virtual images is such that even the most experienced pilot, flying over, would not realize that he was viewing a projection.

VIRTUAL AIRPORT was originally created as part of a flight simulation package for training airline pilots, but it has also been used by airport architects to study the design of existing airports.

Along with the program, the devices needed to make it function were also taken—including several three-dimensional holographic projectors, which use technology that is not yet available to the general public.

The police maintain that the theft of the program and devices was commissioned by a foreign government. I am not convinced. But for lack of any other leads, it makes sense to continue the investigation in this direction.

The inspector, reading over Mickey's shoulder, looked over the image files that had been attached to Minnie's message.

"So there *must* be a connection between the two cases: the theft of the program and the rerouting of the airplanes," declared Burns.

"Exactly! I'm sure we're on to something," Mickey exclaimed.

Just then, Mickey heard the ring of his radio transmitter. He yanked the device from his belt.

Minnie had managed to sneak away, out of sight of the hijackers, and reach one of the landing strips where her radio could get reception.

"Mickey, can you hear me?" she called.

"Minnie, where are you? Have you figured it out?"

"It's very strange," she responded, out of breath. "It *looks* like I am standing on the run-way of our airport, but I *feel* like I'm in the mountains. I can't talk long ... they could find me at any moment."

"Try to describe what you see," Mickey urged. "There are a lot of mountains around the city!"

"From where I am, I can see the side of a

mountain covered with fallen trees, as if there's been an avalanche or a mudslide."

"Sit tight. I'll be there soon," said Mickey as he signed off.

In a flash, Mickey had reached his fighter plane, gotten clearance from the tower, and was taking off, leaving behind a long trail of white smoke.

"Let's hope he doesn't do anything crazy," said Burns with a sigh, watching the plane as it got smaller and smaller until it was only a speck in the sky.

With engines running at full throttle, Mickey flew higher and higher until he had a clear view of the mountains around the city.

"Minnie, can you see me?" he shouted into his radio.

On the edge of a runway, Detective Minnie had managed to hide herself behind a tree.

"Not yet," she responded. "It's too cloudy. Try to fly underneath the clouds."

Decreasing altitude, he dove into the clouds, where visibility was almost zero. But, thanks to his instruments, the plane was able to navigate through the bottom of the thick layer of clouds. Suddenly a vista opened up below him . . . and, there! There were the flattened trees that Minnie must have been talking about. He flew toward them for a closer look.

"I see you! I see you!" Minnie shouted into the radio as she waved her arms.

But Minnie had just made a terrible mistake: her shouts drew the attention of the hijackers, who followed the sound and began to run toward Minnie.

The detective managed to run into the stone building, but the leader of the hijackers, who had noticed the fighter jet flying overhead, was hot on her heels.

"I knew you were trouble the second I saw you!" he shouted. "Give me that radio, now!"

He reached out to grab the device from Minnie, but she stretched out her foot and tripped him. The hijacker fell to the ground, as the rest of the passengers broke into a round of applause.

Minnie leaned over and ripped off the scoundrel's hood. . . .

"Well, well, well, why am I not surprised?" she said.

After his latest escape from prison, it seemed Peg Leg Pete had gone right back to work! He was no stranger to Mickey and Minnie. In fact, Mickey himself had put Pete away several times before by proving the scoundrel's involvement in one crooked scheme after another.

A second later, the ringleader's men had Minnie surrounded.

"Should I tie her up, boss?" one of them asked.

"There's no time!" he replied, scrambling to his feet. "We've been found out. We have to get out of here!"

Minnie could hear Mickey's jet getting closer and closer.

"Load all the gold you can onto my plane," Pete barked to his men. "Quickly!" Then, turning to Minnie, he wagged his finger at her and hissed, "You'll pay for this!"

Chapter 10

FINAL ENCOUNTER

Mickey couldn't believe his eyes. On the plateau just below his plane was an exact replica of the city airport: the control tower, the buildings, the planes parked at the gates—there were even taxis lined up at the taxi stand! It all looked completely real.

"Now I understand how three pilots landed here without suspecting a thing!" Mickey said to himself.

In radio contact with Mickey, Inspector Burns had followed the transmissions between Mickey and Minnie. Then, once Burns had pinpointed the location of

Mickey's plane, he alerted his agents. Together they flew off in several helicopters to find the virtual airport.

Meanwhile, Detective Mickey had begun preparations to land on the plateau. Mickey hesitated for a moment. At the very least, he hoped these runways were real! Otherwise, he was in trouble. But three commercial pilots had landed their planes here safely, so Mickey decided it was worth the risk.

Mickey had to hurry. The hijackers' jet was already beginning its takeoff maneuver. They knew that the police could arrive at any minute.

The detective had no intention of letting them get away. But how could he keep their jet from taking off?

Inside the cockpit of Pete's plane, one of the hijackers gazed out the window and spotted Mickey's plane. "Boss, the fighter plane is landing."

But Pete brushed off the warning. "Power up the engines," he ordered.

Meanwhile, Minnie and the other passengers, no longer guarded by the hijackers, had wandered out of the stone building and were watching the developing scene.

The planes were at opposite ends of the runway: Mickey was coming in for a landing at one end, and Peg Leg Pete was preparing for takeoff on the other. The tension was high. Detective Minnie held her breath and covered her eyes.

"Boss, he's coming right at us!" screamed one of the hijackers inside Pete's plane. The fighter plane had touched down and was hurtling down the runway, straight at their jet! The hijacker slammed on the brakes with all his might, but a collision seemed inevitable. Pete and all his men ran toward the tail end of the plane. There was not enough time to open the emergency exit, but at least the impact would be less violent in the tail.

Moments later, the planes hit each other head-on. Peg Leg Pete's larger plane upended Mickey's fighter and flipped it over on the runway!

Just then, several helicopters full of police officers swooped down from out of the sky

and landed a safe distance from the crash site.

The hijackers, who had managed to get out of the jet with only bumps and bruises, were immediately surrounded, unmasked, and arrested by the police.

"Well, look who we have here!" exclaimed Burns. He had singled out one of the hijackers, a small man wearing glasses. "Paul Egler, aka 'the Eagle,' criminal computer whiz."

Detective Minnie came running over to fill in the inspector on her latest findings. "Peg Leg Pete is behind the entire operation!" she exclaimed. Then, looking at Egler, she added, "We should have known that Pete would have you working for him, after you two met in prison."

Speaking of Peg Leg Pete, there was no sign of him. And Mickey was nowhere to be found either!

"Look carefully!" the inspector said to his men, worried about his friend. "We must find him!"

The small fighter plane had definitely taken the brunt of the crash. Amid all the wreckage, it took some time for the police to reach the cockpit. If Detective Mickey had ended up underneath all that, thought the inspector, he might not be in very good shape....

All of a sudden, a shout rang out. It was one of the police officers. "Careful! There's a fuel leak! The plane might explode!"

Burns understood that the risk for his men was too great, so he called off the search, and ordered them away from the plane.

And not a moment too soon . . . as a tremendous explosion tossed both planes into the air. The thunderous sound echoed off of the surrounding mountains.

Minnie gasped in horror and buried her face in the inspector's lapel.

But all of a sudden, they heard a voice call out from the perimeter of the runway. "Could somebody help me down from here?"

"Mickey?" Minnie and Burns exclaimed in unison.

They turned toward the voice, and there, clinging to the top of a pine tree on the edge of the runway, was Mickey, his parachute entangled in its branches. For a moment, the inspector stood rooted to the ground in utter amazement. Then he came back to his senses and ordered his officers to help Mickey down.

"Whoever invented the ejector seat . . . I owe 'em one!" declared Mickey, once he was safely on the ground. "And same goes for the inventor of the parachute."

Minnie ran to hug him—she had been convinced that Mickey was gone!

"I warned you not to get that pilot's license!" Minnie scolded good-naturedly. "Look at the mess you got yourself into!"

Then, all three of them—Mickey, Minnie, and Burns—turned at the sound of a shout. "Come on, you rascal, move it!"

To their surprise, there was Aunt Rita, pushing Peg Leg Pete toward them, his wrists tied behind him with the strap of her purse.

"This criminal was taking advantage of all the confusion to attempt an escape. But I kept my eye on him. I respectfully hand him over to you, Inspector. I'm sure you'll know what to do with him!"

"Put him in the helicopter with the others," Burns said to his officers. Then, full of admiration, he came over to Aunt Rita. "Ma'am, you are truly amazing!"

"Oh, go on . . . you're making me blush," she replied.

The other passengers gathered around Aunt Rita, thanking her once again for her courage throughout their ordeal. One passenger in particular was very generous with the compliments—none other than Mr. Bauble!

"I think I owe you an apology," he said sheepishly. "I'm afraid I was pretty rude to you."

This time, Aunt Rita really did turn red.

"And just so you know that my apology is sincere," he continued, reaching into his inside jacket pocket, "I beg you to accept this little gift."

Aunt Rita took a small red velvet box from Mr. Bauble's outstretched hand. Inside was a magnificent emerald ring!

Later, after all of the passengers had been taken home, the police officers were able to reclaim the stolen computer program and locate the holographic projectors that Peg Leg Pete and Egler had situated on one of the mountainsides. All of the stolen property would be returned to the aeronautic base in Software Valley.

Once the projectors were turned off and the virtual images were gone, all that remained of the phony airport was a runway